D1383145

3-9

THE SCIENTIFIC KNOWLEDGE
OF PHYSICAL NATURE

Section de Philosophie
Nº 2

JOSEPH J. SIKORA, S. J.

THE SCIENTIFIC KNOWLEDGE OF PHYSICAL NATURE

An Essay on the Distinction between the Philosophy of Nature and Physical Science

DESCLÉE DE BROUWER
BRUGES - PARIS
1966

Imprimi potest Oak Park, Illinois, January 20, 1965
John R. CONNERY S. J.
Provincial

Imprimatur Montreal, March 8, 1965
Lawrence P. WHELAN
Vicar General

PREFACE

If progress in philosophy takes place, as Maritain says, by ever deepening insight (and consequent growth of the systematization of insight) rather than by the mere substitution of one scheme of explanation for another, the importance of a continuing and progressive philosophical tradition is evident. Since the Thomist acknowledges the presence of an ontological mystery into which we can penetrate ever more deeply to know it in itself and not just in schematic formulas of the intellect, he must expect a continuing development in the Thomist tradition.

But this process of growth is "organic"—what was there remains even while expanding its being. Hence it is necessary to retain the solid achievements of earlier Thomists even while attaining new aspects of the real. To do otherwise would be to lose, perhaps, more than we gain.

The opportunity for such an advancement of Thomist thought in the presence of the new, so-called "empiriological" sciences has not been missed by Thomists such as Jacques Maritain. It is the purpose of this essay to elaborate and to clarify the distinction drawn by Maritain between the philosophy of nature and modern physical science, in the light of the Thomist tradition. But this is not simply an attempt to reproduce the doctrine of Maritain; this is not just an essay in the history of philosophy but an essay in philosophy itself. The debt to Maritain is obvious; but the responsibility for what is said, and especially for what is new, must not be laid on him but on the writer.

My aim in all this can be summed up as *vetera novis augere*. I believe that what Maritain has done is to capture genuine insights of Hume and Kant and their disciples concerning the knowledge of phenomena, and to assimilate these to the Thomist synthesis. I propose to push a little farther the work he has begun.

Some Thomists may object that this is an impossible work for a Thomist. If contemporary Thomism is only an archaeological study, they are of course quite right ; for St. Thomas knew little of phenomenal knowledge, or at least of a *science* of phenomena. But such a view of Thomism in fact denies the presence of that ontological mystery and philosophical progress of which we spoke above. Its result is not to arrest the dynamism of the human spirit, which is irresistible, but to delay the assimilation to Thomism of new insights which have there their natural home, of the new insights which are more evident to many moderns than the old insights are. But in the face of such delay, is it any wonder that some Thomists have been left to talk to themselves while the world goes on in the search for knowledge ?

And yet it is not an adequate answer to such philosophical provincialism to forget the heritage of traditional thought in order to seek only the new. What is to happen on the day after tomorrow, when this "new" has itself become old ? The philosophy of nature has suffered a general eclipse among modern philosophers (with some happy exceptions). There are even so-called Thomists who leave the domain of nature entirely to the modern sciences. But the philosophy of nature does not rest on a mere "optical illusion" of the intellect. It has its own autonomous existence as a scientific knowledge alongside and yet beyond the modern natural sciences, and indeed even interacts with them in many ways (see Appendix II).

In order to discuss the distinction between scientific knowledges, it will be necessary for us to consider at some length the nature of science itself. The question of the nature of scientific knowledge is sometimes approached from the point of view of the methods of reasoning employed, since human science is permeated with discursive activity, with reasoning. But if reasoning is necessary for human science, it must be seen to be only a necessary *means*. For all knowledge, scientific or otherwise, is ultimately a *seeing*. The intellect sees ; but in science the insight of the intellect has special characteristics, which we shall see later. We should not determine the nature of scientific knowledge primarily from the mode of reasoning employed but from the mode of insight achieved.

In focusing our attention upon the scientific mode of insight rather than of discursive reasoning we may hope to avoid some difficulties which arise from narrow, relatively a priori conceptions of the logic of science. From this point of view, it will become necessary later to supplement traditional conceptions of the logic of science in the face of scientific knowledge which does not follow the logical method of the *Posterior Analytics* of Aristotle. But this latter point will not be followed up in this essay. Here our concern is centered on the method of abstractive visualization and the formal object of such visualization proper to the philosophy of nature and to physical science.

The narrowness of the subject is, however, balanced by its fundamental importance for philosophy. If it is true, as Thomists insist, that the philosophical knowledge of the physical world is the necessary basis for all our philosophizing in other areas, then it is most important to understand the relationship of the philosophy of nature and physical science. If this is not properly understood, the so-called "conflict between science and philosophy" can only persist, to the ultimate detriment of both. But the primary question to be answered in order to achieve such an understanding is that of the formal object of the philosophy of nature and of physical science, since this is the ultimate norm for the distinction and specification of sciences in Thomist thought. The whole of this essay is directed toward answering this question. However, lest all my effort to establish a sharp distinction between these knowledges be misunderstood to indicate that no interaction between them takes place, I have added an outline sketch of some manners in which such interaction does in fact take place (see Appendix II).

This essay was originally written in the form of a doctoral dissertation at the University of Notre Dame. The dissertation was written under the direction of Vincent Smith, who disagreed on fundamental points but showed the utmost tolerance in his direction. The original work has undergone a thorough revision, and the two Appendices have been added.

I have seen fit to drop the bibliography. The original bibliography would now be inadequate and it does not seem possible to trace the various influences in the seven years since the completion of the original dissertation. To replace it I have added a very brief summary bibliography.

Special thanks are due to Messrs. David Stagaman, S.J., Frank Molony, S.J., and Daniel Perrine, S.J., who aided in proofreading and preparing the indices, but above all to R. P. Jean D'Aragon, S.J., editor of *Essais pour notre temps*.

CONTENTS

CHAPTER I

INTRODUCTION

The purpose of this essay is to delineate clearly the distinction between the philosophy of nature and physical science in the framework of the Thomist tradition. It is the opinion of this writer that this tradition is best represented for the work at hand by the line of development proceeding through Cajetan, John of St. Thomas, and Maritain. Consequently, an effort will be made to be faithful to that "branch" of the tradition. But it must be noted that this is more than a mere statement of positions already developed elsewhere. I hope to *elaborate*, and thereby to confirm, the doctrine of Maritain concerning the distinction between the philosophy of nature and physical science. The inspiration for this essay most certainly is from St. Thomas, Cajetan, John of St. Thomas, and Maritain. But it is at the same time an *essay* toward something new, the responsibility for which is mine alone.

The investigation will proceed along two lines, after a preliminary historical discussion of the tradition we have spoken of. First we will take a second-intentional point of view and examine the nature of the *knowledge* attained in each of these sciences, giving special attention to the *method* of abstractive visualization. Then we shall turn to the *object* to which this visualization refers, and in terms of which we hope to make clear the distinction between these sciences. We shall not attempt here to review critically other traditions within the Thomist school. These I hope to consider elsewhere.

But before beginning, it is necessary to make clear what is meant by (1) the philosophy of nature, (2) physical science, (3) method, (4) object. It will also be necessary to show, in a summary way, how the philosophy of nature is distinguished from metaphysics.

A. WHAT IS THE PHILOSOPHY OF NATURE ?

Although "philosophy of nature" is practically an equivocal term by reason of the diversity of problems which have been studied under its name, especially in the modern period, we can considerably simplify the task of defining it be restricting our understanding of the term to that of the "Aristotelians" and the "Aristotelian-Thomists."[1] Even among these one will find differences regarding the status of the philosophy of nature in relation to other knowledges, and even in its very problematic. But, in any event, it is at least agreed that the problematic of the philosophy of nature includes that of the *Physics* of Aristotle, whether or not this problematic may have been expanded with justification, either by Aristotle himself in other works or by later philosophers.

The solutions given by Aristotle to the problems posed may not be accepted by all, or, in some cases, by any ; but the Aristotelian-Thomistic school has consistently recognized at least the problems themselves as genuine and as belonging to a philosophical enquiry about nature. This is as true of St. Thomas Aquinas,[2] Cajetan,[3] John of St. Thomas,[4] and Jacques Maritain[5] as it was of Aristotle.

---

1. When I use the term "Aristotelian-Thomist", I do not intend it to describe all who would agree to be called Thomists. The Aristotelian-Thomist recognizes the fundamentally Aristotelian aspects of the thought of St. Thomas. Some have so emphasized the non-Aristotelian character of Thomistic metaphysics as to almost forget the Aristotelian character of Thomistic philosophy of nature. But it is beyond the scope of this essay to dwell on this point.

2. See the Commentary of St. Thomas on the *Physics* of Aristotle. There are several editions of this text : it is to be found in the Vives, Parma, and Leonine texts of St. Thomas and in various independent editions. We have employed the Pirotta edition of 1953 published by D'Auria of Naples.

3. See *Thomae de Vio Cajetani Tractatus De Subjecto Naturalis Philosophiae*, ed. C. De Koninck and R. P. E. Gaudron, O. F. M. (Laval, Quebec, 1939).

4. See JOHN OF ST. THOMAS, *Cursus Philosophicus*, ed. Reiser (Taurini, 1933), II, Part I, Question I, Article I.

5. See Jacques MARITAIN, *Scholasticism and Politics* (New York, 1938), pp. 54-55, and his *La Philosophie de la Nature* (Paris, 1937), p. 112.

What are these problems ? In the *Physics*, we find that the central problem is to achieve a scientific knowledge[1] of the mobile as such, of being which undergoes motion, precisely as such. Motion must be understood, however, not in the usual modern sense of local motion ; rather it is the "act of a being in potency insofar as it is in potency," as Aristotle says in *Gamma Physicorum*, 1, 201a 10-11. This definition applies to all change which we can *directly* observe in the physical universe, whether it be qualitative in nature, purely quantitative, or local motion (see *Epsilon Physicorum*, 1, 225b 7-9). In a secondary sense, motion is also taken to include generation and corruption, the processes by which substances change, one into another (see *Gamma Physicorum*, 1, 201a, 11-15). Such change is known only *indirectly* through motion in the strict sense.

Since to know scientifically means, for Aristotle, to know the cause,[2] the problem is to know the causes of motion. But this involves knowing not only the intrinsic causes of motion, the so-called "principles of nature" which enter into the very constitution of motion itself,[3] not only the extrinsic causes of motion—those factors extrinsic to the motion itself, but contributing to its being[4]—but also the attributes and conditions of motion—the infinite,[5] place,[6] the void, if such exists,[7] time.[8] It requires knowing the various kinds[9] and parts[10] of motion, and culminates in the attempt to reduce all the diverse motions of the mobile universe to the unity of the Prime Mover or Movers.[11]

---

1. Greek, *epistasthae ;* Latin, *scire.*
2. *Alpha Analyticorum Posteriorum*, 2, 71b, 9-12.
3. *Alpha, Beta Physicorum ; Gamma Physicorum*, 1-3.
4. *Ibid.*
5. *Gamma Physicorum*, 4-8.
6. *Delta Physicorum*, 1-5.
7. *Delta Physicorum*, 6-9.
8. *Delta Physicorum*, 10-14.
9. *Epsilon Physicorum.*
10. *Zeta Physicorum.*
11. *Eta, Theta Physicorum.*

Aristotle himself,[1] and St. Thomas[2] as well, conceive the philosophy of nature to extend itself further into the domains of the various particular kinds of motion in the world, attempting to know, so far as is possible, the particular causes as well as the general causes. Indeed, ideally, the philosophy of nature should know the proper natures of the diverse kinds of mobile beings.

Whether or not the problematic of the philosophy of nature actually should be extended into the detail of the physical universe, it is quite clear that the central concern of the Aristotelian-Thomistic philosophy of nature is with motion. The problem is to understand the opposition of sameness and otherness which is seen in what we call motion. And this does not mean just to construct some mental scheme of explanation, but to *see* the real causes of motion.

Let this then serve as our preliminary nominal definition of the philosophy of nature : it is the science which studies the motion of things, with a view to seeing its real causes, characteristics, and conditions, at least the most universal.

B. WHAT IS PHYSICAL SCIENCE ?

Just as with the philosophy of nature, we should obtain a preliminary nominal definition of physical science.   Here again we find differences of opinion concerning the problematic.   This is especially true if we consider the history of physical science.

What is now called physical science originated[3] in the sixteenth and seventeenth centuries, especially with the work of Copernicus, Kepler, Brahe, and Galileo in the realm

1. On Aristotle's general method, see *Alpha Physicorum*, 1.   See St. Thomas Aquinas on the order of the Aristotelian treatises in the philosophy of nature, in his commentary on the first book of the *Physics*, lecture 1, number 7.

2. St. Thomas Aquinas, *In De Sensu et Sensato*, lectio 1, number 2.   This text, despite its presence in a commentary, clearly reflects the mind of St. Thomas himself.

3. This must not be understood absolutely.   Modern science can trace its roots back far beyond the sixteenth century.   See, for example, Pierre Duhem's ten volume work on this subject, *Le Système du Monde* (Paris, 1913-1959).

of astronomy, and of Galileo, Descartes, and Newton in the realm of what is today called physics. To undertake an adequate historical account of the development of physical science and its gradual realization of its own proper nature would be the task of a multi-volume work. There are a number of works which are helpful to read in this regard ;[1] but perhaps the task of describing in detail the historical evolution of physical science yet remains to be satisfactorily accomplished, from a philosophical point of view.

Instead of attempting to understand what physical science is in terms of its history, it would be easier to consider it as existing here and now. Necessarily this will require a severe limitation on the pretensions of this discussion ; for, if physical science actually has undergone a long and complex evolution, we may with justification believe that any definition arrived at by a consideration of its existing state will not be adequate for its past, or, perhaps, for its future. [2]

There are differences even today concerning the problematic of physical science. Some would have it treat problems which are thought by others to be altogether outside the scope of the science. Compare, for example, Eddington,[3] Jeans,[4] and de Broglie[5] with Mach,[6] Schlick,[7] Ayer,[8] and

1. See, for example, H. BUTTERFIELD, *The Origins of Modern Science* (New York, 1951) ; W. D. DAMPIER, *A History of Science* (New York, 1946) ; Sir James JEANS, *The Growth of Physical Science* (Cambridge, 1951).

2. This does not mean, of course, that the mode of knowing reality which is today known as physical science will in any fundamental way be altered, but only that it is conceivable that other modes of approach to physical reality might some day prove feasible and deserving of the name "physical science".

3. A. S. EDDINGTON, *The Nature of the Physical World* (New York, 1929).

4. J. JEANS, *The Mysterious Universe* (New York, 1930); *Physics and Philosophy* (New York, 1943).

5. L. DE BROGLIE, *Continu et Discontinu en Physique Moderne* (Paris, 1941), pp. 67-76.

6. E. MACH, *The Science of Mechanics*, trans. T. J. McCormack (Chicago, 1893).

7. M. SCHLICK, *Philosophy of Nature*, trans. A. von Zeppelin (New York, 1949), p. 21.

8. A. J. AYER, *Language, Truth, and Logic* (New York).

the other positivists. We find Eddington, Jeans, de Broglie, and many others speculating about the need for a God or the ultimate nature of the physical universe, and many other subsidiary topics which the positivists insist have no place anywhere at all, least of all in physical science. The former group appears to consider such problems as actually within the scope of physical science itself, at least in some way.

But may we not find some point of agreement, some common problematic, some general characteristics acceptable to all ? Clearly there must be such, since these men on both sides, as well as those who belong to neither group (perhaps the great majority of working scientists), are capable of working together, of communicating, of progressing in something which all agree is physical science.

The principal parts of physical science are physics and chemistry, to which we might also add geology and astronomy. This division is, of course, rapidly disappearing, as all these parts tend to merge into one physical science. In this treatise we shall consider physical science as meaning physics, which is in fact physical science *par excellence*, the model toward which all the other parts tend.

Physics, like the philosophy of nature, seems to be concerned with motion. It studies the flux of electrical and magnetic fields, the radiation of light, heat transfer, the laws of falling bodies, the laws of acoustics, cloud-chamber phenomena, and many other such motions in the universe. The physicist is clearly trying to get an explanation of these things, but his explanation, as we shall see, is given in terms of hypothesis and theory, rather than of the ontological causes of things.

The physicist discovers facts and laws in his experience and attempts to "explain" them all in terms of some unifying theory. For example, the laws of falling bodies were discovered by Galileo,[1] while observations of the motions of the planets

---

1. Galileo GALILEI, *Dialogues Concerning Two New Sciences*, trans. H. Crew and A. De Salvio (New York), pp. 264 ff.

were interpreted by Kepler's three laws of planetary motion. [1]
It remained for Newton to bring these two sets of laws together in his theory of universal gravitation. [2] So also electro-
magnetic and radiation phenomena were brought together
in Maxwell's electromagnetic theory of light. We have seen
the work of unification accomplished by the modern atomic
theories of Bohr, Heisenberg, de Broglie, Schrodinger, etc. ;
and we are now witnessing attempts to unify electromagnetic
and gravitational phenomena under some all-embracing
theory.

But, as we have indicated, the hypotheses and theories
of the physicist do not give us ontological insight. Rather,
he has merely made an "interpretation" and unification of the
data. Whether this interpretation is regarded as having
more than a purely logical significance depends on which
physicist one cares to consult. If we ask de Broglie, Jeans,
Eddington, or some other such, we will be told that these
"interpretations" are at least clues to the nature of things.
If we consult a positivist, we will be told that, since there are
no natures to know anyway, obviously there cannot be any
ontological significance in physical theory.

The *problematic* of the philosophy of nature and of physical
science is then, in a way, the same. Both seek an understanding
of motion, both seek to give a reason for it ; but this understanding is sought in radically different ways. St. Thomas
Aquinas, although he was not confronted with modern science,
yet may have been aware of these two modes of understanding. [3]

But before we can state clearly just what we mean now
by physical science, it is necessary to make one more precision.
Physical science is to be distinguished from biological science,
which concerns itself with the motions of living things. Physical science may consider these very same motions ; but when
it does they are given no special place above the motions of the

---

1. J. KEPLER, *De Stella Martis ; Harmonices Mundi libri v.*
2. Isaac NEWTON, *Mathematical Principles of Natural Philosophy*, trans.
F. Cajori (Berkeley, 1947), pp. 406-417.
3. *Summa Theologiae*, Part I, Question 32, article 1.

inanimate.   We may say that they are no longer considered *as* motions of the animate, but rather simply as physical motion.

With this, we are now prepared to give a nominal definition of physical science, as the science which studies the motion in the universe with a view to evolving hypothetical accounts, which serve to bring many motions into a *unity of knowledge*, without in any way giving any special ontological preeminence to any particular kind of motion.

Some may, as we have said, see in these hypothetical accounts some kind of indirect ontological significance.   But this point shall be discussed below.

It should be noted that, as we progress in our understanding of the philosophy of nature and of physical science, it may become necessary to reconsider and reinterpret what has been said above only by way of introduction.

C. METHOD

Our inquiry first concerns the method of visualization in the philosophy of nature and in physical science.   All knowing reduces to immediate "seeing", mediate "discourse of reason", or "faith".   Clearly, as regards fully *scientific* knowledge by *natural* human reason, there can be no question of faith.   The aim of such scientific knowledge is to *see* a multiplicity of facts in the unity of a cause or causes.[1]   Such knowledge is not given to us by nature, to be immediately "seen".   We are confronted with multiplicity, the cause of which is not evident.   It is necessary for our reason to "move" from this to the unifying principles.   This process is called "discourse of reason".   But if discourse of reason is required, then there must be a way to follow in the pursuit of scientific truth in general and in special domains of being as well.   The way after truth, the proper form of discourse of reason, is called

---

1. ARISTOTLE, *Beta Physicorum*, 3, 194b 16-23.

the correct "method". This term is derived from the Greek *"methodos"*, which comes from *"hodos"* (way) and *"meta"* (after).

It should be noted that method can be understood in various senses. The general study of the method of attaining scientific knowledge belongs to logic. This general study may be concerned with the fundamental forms which discourse of reason takes, which are partially treated, for example, in the *Prior Analytics* of Aristotle ; this is one part of formal logic. But this general discussion is only the first part of formal logic. Modern logic has unveiled countless particular and detailed forms which reduce to the most general, but which are not seen in the mere contemplation of the general forms themselves.

The general study of method may also mean the study of the preparation of matter for the discourse of reason. Here the nature of conceptualization of judgment, of the presentation of the data by the senses, of the objective requirements of the premises of an inference, of the various general kinds of matter, are studied. Our concern here is still with discourse, but now in its reference to that which is discoursed about. This new concern distinguishes this study adequately from formal logic ; but it is also distinct from psychology, which itself is concerned with reasoning and with other aspects of knowledge in their relation to the reasoning *subject*, i. e., man. The study of the proper disposition of matter for discourse is partially treated in the *Posterior Analytics* of Aristotle ; we may call it material logic.

Beyond general and special formal logic and general material logic, there remains the vast domain of *methodology*, the study of the particular preparations for and mode of reasoning in each of the special sciences. The need of methodology is evident. Preparations must be made for reasoning, because the real does not come into our intellect naturally in a suitable form for scientific reasoning. Moreover, the matter is presented in diverse manners in diverse sciences, as in theology and philosophy, ethics and metaphysics, and, as we shall see, in the philosophy of nature and the natural sciences.   This necessitates some differences in preparation and in the reasoning itself.   The same matter may well be adaptable to diverse modes of reasoning, as in mathematics and metaphysics, in ethics and theology.   Therefore the preparation for discourse of reason cannot be accomplished in an altogether univocal manner, but in a manner suitable to the object of each particular science ; the same must be said of the very discourse itself.

In summary then, we have the following schema for logic :

Logic—the study of the discourse of reason
   Formal logic—the study of the discourse of reason in its formal character as a discourse
      General formal logic—the study of the general forms of the discourse of reason
      Special formal logic—the study of special forms of the discourse of reason
         as constructed by the intellect
         as abstracted by the intellect from the determinate subject-matter of special sciences—*formal methodology.*
   Material logic—the study of the discourse of reason in its relation to its matter
      General material logic—the study of the general preparation of matter for discourse of reason
      Special material logic—the study of the special preparation of matter, in particular areas of study, for the discourse of reason—*material methodology.*

Although psychology likewise studies the discourse of reason, as indicated above, it is not concerned *per se* with this discourse but rather with the subject who is discoursing, i. e., man as a living being, in his formal character as living, to which pertains his power of discursive thought.   On the other hand, logic is concerned *per se* with this discourse, both formal logic, in which this is evident, and material logic, which is concerned with the preparation for reasoning—

thereby obviously receiving its intelligibility from the very discourse itself.

We do not intend in this essay to give a complete exposition of the method of the philosophy of nature or of physical science. For our purposes, it is sufficient to examine the method of intellectual visualization. The mode of discourse will follow upon and be in accordance with the mode of visualization, since vision is the principle of discourse. Moreover, the study of the mode of visualization is sufficient to see the differentiation of the sciences, as we shall see.

The subject of this essay therefore can be said to pertain to *material logic*, in so far as it concerns the *method* of visualization in diverse sciences. But when we turn to consider the *objects* of sciences, as transcending the intellect and as imposing the distinction of sciences on the intellect from the very nature of the things themselves, then we are in *metaphysics*. The study of *methods* is a study of second intentions—the intellect reflects on itself ; but the study of *objects* in their transcendent content is a study of first intentions—the intellect considers reality under the light of being. The close relationship between these two studies will become apparent in chapter five.

D. THE DISTINCTION OF THE PHILOSOPHY OF NATURE FROM METAPHYSICS

We have spoken above of the problematic of the philosophy of nature, and have seen it to be concerned with the ontological principles of motion, both intrinsic and extrinsic to the mobile being. But to say that there is a well-defined problem of the philosophy of nature is not yet to say that the philosophy of nature is a distinct and autonomous science.

In actual fact, as has been pointed out by Maritain,[1] the philosophy of nature has led a rather precarious existence.

1. *La Philosophie de la Nature*, p. 1.

It has been in danger of assimilation either by metaphysics on one hand or by the natural sciences (physical and biological) on the other.[1] It is necessary therefore to consider, in at least a summary way, the grounds for clearly distinguishing the philosophy of nature from metaphysics.

To secure principles in terms of which to make this distinction, we may consider the doctrine of St. Thomas Aquinas concerning the distinction of the sciences.

St. Thomas indicates that the first great division of science is into speculative and practical science. The aim of speculative science is simply the contemplation of truth for its own sake, while that of practical science is ultimately the direction of activity.[2] Clearly, in view of what we have said above about its problematic, the philosophy of nature is a speculative science. It is necessary then to examine the grounds for distinguishing speculative sciences from each other. The doctrine of St. Thomas on this point is to be found in various texts, but chiefly in his *Commentary on Boethius' On The Trinity*, Question 5, article 1.[3] Our discussion is based principally on this text.

It is a cardinal principle for St. Thomas that powers, habits, and acts are diversified according to the diversification of the object, taken in the formal sense of object.[4]

We shall not pause to consider the notion of "object" in its general significance ; it is, however, necessary to understand what is meant by the object of the cognitive power, habit, or act. We shall consider directly only the object of the cognitive act. What we say can be applied, *mutatis mutandis*, to the object of a cognitive habit or power ; for these are ordered toward cognitive acts, and the object of the act is at once also the object of the habit and power. Also, our consideration will be restricted to human intellectual acts. It will

---

1. *Ibid.*
2. *Commentary on Book Eleven of the Metaphysics*, lect. 7, number 2265.
3. See also *In De Sensu et Sensato*, lect. 1 ; *In I Phys.*, lect. 1 ; *Summ. Theol.*, I, q. 85, a. 1, ad 2.
4. *Summ. Theol.*, I, q. 1, a. 3, c. ; q. 77, a. 3, c.

apply proportionally, however, to sense knowledge as well.

The human soul, through the intellect, strives to become all things. It does this by bringing the "other" into a union with the "self". But this is not accomplished by destroying the otherness of the other, as happens in the assimilation of food. Rather, here the other remains other even while coming into communion with the intellect. This mysterious action whereby the intellect feeds on the other and yet leaves it intact in its otherness is called "intentional union".

Thus the intellect may be conceived as in some sense "outgoing", seeking the other to bring it within itself as other. When, in its outward movement, it finds an other "thrust up against" *(ob-jectum)* itself, it pauses to bring this other fully into itself, at least as fully as possible. Thus the *objectum*, or object, is said to terminate the act of the intellect, inasmuch as the movement outward finds here momentary rest in contemplation.

The object, then, stands off as in some way other than, opposite to, the intellect and the knowing "subject", even in the very act of knowing. But ordinarily, this object contains far more intelligibility than is revealed to the first glance of the intellect. Its being is a fountain of intelligibility from which the intellect can drink ever more deeply. The intellect comes to this object in different ways, through many conceptualizations, because no one concept is adequate to exhaust the intelligibility of the being or even to provide an "opening" through which the total intelligibility may be drawn into the intellect.

Thus the object may be considered in two ways : it may be the thing in its complete and inexhaustible (for us) intelligibility, or it may be precisely that "part" or perfection of the thing which momentarily terminates the outgoing movement of the intellect in contemplation, and through which, perhaps, some considerable portion of the total intelligibility may be seen (but only by the long continued ever deepening gaze of the intellect, and, if possible, with the help of "scientific demonstration").

The first of these two kinds of object is what scholastics have traditionally meant by the term "material object". It is the second which is the "formal object" of scholastic philosophy, the "formal determination of the object" [1] of St. Thomas Aquinas.

Later on in this chapter, we shall observe the gradual clarification of this notion of formal object accomplished in the later scholastic tradition. But for the moment we return to the doctrine of St. Thomas Aquinas concerning the distinction of the sciences.

For St. Thomas, the common object of the intellect is being, [2] although its proper object (that which it attains of itself directly and primarily [3]) is the quiddity existing in corporeal matter. [4] But the intellect, in its movement towards real being, is confronted with a multifaceted reality, a reality which, by reason of its overflowing intelligibility, beckons to the intellect in many diverse ways. In order for the intellect to attain this reality in its multiplicity of aspects, there is need for many diverse intellectual movements toward it. In order that we may intellectually possess this reality in a stable and permanent manner, that we may discourse about it with relative facility, it is necessary that several *habits*—several *sciences*—be acquired respecting its various facets. The diversity of these habits will be known to us, as was already said above, from the specific diversity to be found within the common object of speculative knowledge—being.

But it is obviously not through just any diversity of being that we have a diversity of speculative science ; rather we must look, as St. Thomas says, for those differences discernible

---

1. *Summ. Theol.*, I, q. 1, a. 3, c. : "... rationem formalem obiecti."

2. *Summ. Theol.*, I. q. 79, a. 7, c. : "Intellectus autem respicit suum obiectum secundum communem rationem entis ; eo quod intellectus possibilis est *quo est omnia fieri.*"

3. *Summ. Theol.*, I, q. 85, a. 8, c. : "id quod est primo et per se cognitum a virtute cognoscitiva, est proprium eius obiectum..."

4. *Summ. Theol.*, I, q. 84, a. 7, c. : "Intellectus autem humani, qui est coniunctus corpori, proprium obiectum est quidditas sive natura in materia corporali existens."

in being precisely in so far as it is an object of speculative science,[1] those differences which are inevitably manifested because of the very nature of scientific knowledge itself.

As St. Thomas points out, by the very fact that the object of speculative science is an object of speculative science, two characteristics necessarily belong to it. Inasmuch as speculative science is in the intellect—which is immaterial—immateriality will be a characteristic of the object itself;[2] for whatever is received is received after the manner of the recipient. Inasmuch as there is truly science—necessary truth[3]—the object will possess an inherent immobility or unchangingness.[4] If, then, we can discern grades of immateriality and immobility in the object of speculative science, in being as known speculatively, we shall have discerned grades of speculative science, general divisions.[5]

In fact, St. Thomas distinguishes three such grades of immateriality. First, one may consider the being which is realized in the physical universe as mobile, subject to constant becoming. This being, individualized in sensible matter, is not of itself subject to intellectual knowledge. But by the process of abstraction, in which individual sensible matter is left out of consideration, this being becomes a fit object of intellectual contemplation. Along with this degree of immateriality, there is also found a corresponding degree of immobility, since matter is the principle of mobility. But we have not yet escaped matter and motion entirely, since we are contemplating the common intelligible principles of mobile being. These principles cannot even be conceived without a relation to motion. This is the level of what St. Thomas calls natural science *(scientia naturalis)*.[6] It is clearly here that we find the philosophy of nature.

1. *In De Trinitate*, q. 5, a. 1.
2. *Ibid.*
3. *Ibid.*
4. *Ibid.*
5. *Ibid.*
6. *Ibid.*

But the intellect may abstract further, setting aside all that by which we can know the intelligible principles of mobile being as mobile, all common sensible matter—matter as subject to sensible qualities. [1] Leaving all this out of consideration, we rise to a new degree of immateriality and consequently to a new degree of immobility—to a new degree of scientific knowledge distinct from *scientia naturalis*. Here is considered being which is realized in the physical universe, but there is no longer any consideration of its actual mode of existence in the physical universe as subjected in sensible matter and subject to motion. [2]

What we are now considering is being divested of all sensible qualities manifestative of nature ; we are left with mere quantified being, being which is said to contain only common intelligible matter—matter as subject to quantity. [3] This is the level of what St. Thomas calls mathematics *(mathematica)*. [4] We are not yet in the metaphysical realm.

Only when the intellect makes a further abstraction, now no longer considering being as quantified but in its mere being, have we come to metaphysics. Completely leaving matter out of consideration, and consequently reaching the sphere of the completely immobile, we come to a science distinct in its object from both *scientia naturalis* and *mathematica*. This object is being which is capable of being realized in matter, but which is also capable (subject to establishment of the fact) of being realized in spirit as well ; since matter is not contained in its intelligibility. [5]

Thus being, in so far as it comes into our intellects, presents three generic facets ; consequently we can distinguish three generic degrees of speculative science.

But perhaps it would be well to point out in somewhat greater detail the difference between the object of the philos-

---

1. *Summ. Theol.*, I, q. 85, a. 1, ad 2.
2. *In De Trinitate*, q. 5, a. 1.
3. *Summ. Theol.*, I, q. 85, a. 1, ad 2.
4. *In De Trinitate*, q. 5, a. 1.
5. *Ibid.*

ophy of nature and that of metaphysics. Clearly, the only being that we know directly is mobile being, for our only immediate meeting with reality is through the senses, which open out to a world shot through with mobility. Both the philosophy of nature and metaphysics must begin with this mobile being. But metaphysics and the philosophy of nature differ in their object ; they each see this mobile being in a different way.

As St. Thomas points out in the *De Ente et Essentia*,[1] the fact that we can conceive all of *what* a man is without knowing *that* he is, a fact which is made even clearer by considering the imaginary phoenix, whose complete essence is known but whose existence is not, indicates that existence is other than essence. This analysis, in effect, presents us with a new dimension even of mobile being, that of existence. Mobile being thus presents two aspects to us, that of its essence, in which are contained the roots of its mobility—matter and form,[2] and that of its existence, the ultimate actuality of being.[3] Later in metaphysics it becomes clear that neither essence nor existence is restricted to the sphere of the mobile, but this is not seen at the outset. At the beginning, the philosophy of nature pursues the problem of the principles of mobility of mobile being, rising up to the Immobile, while metaphysics pursues the problem of the principles of the existence of mobile being, rising up to the Pure Existence.

At the start, the object of metaphysics is not actually distinguished according to a higher degree of immateriality from that of the philosophy of nature, but only virtually. Because metaphysics is concerned with the principles of existence, because its object is being (*per accidens* mobile) as existing, and because in fact existence is not confined to mobile

---

1. Text in Roland-Gosselin, Le *"De Ente et Essentia" de S. Thomas d'Aquin* (Kain, Belgium, 1926). Chapter four, p. 34, lines 7-15.

2. *De Ente et Essentia*, c. 2, pp. 6-10.

3. *Summ. Theol.*, I, q. 4, a. 1, ad 3 : "Dicendum quod ipsum esse est perfectissimum omnium ; comparatur enim ad omnia ut actus. Nihil enim habet actualitatem, nisi inquantum est ; unde ipsum esse est actualitas omnium rerum, et etiam ipsarum formarum."

being and will later be seen as such, the object of metaphysics can properly be said to be being in so far as it is being *(ens in quantum ens)* even though it is not *known* to transcend matter and motion until later on in the inquiry. On the other hand, the object of the philosophy of nature can be formulated as mobile being in so far as it is mobile *(ens mobile in quantum mobile)* with understanding of the full meaning of this formula right from the beginning.

Thus it might be more proper to contrast the object of the philosophy of nature with that of metaphysics in the following manner :

> Beginning of inquiry
>> philosophy of nature—mobile being in so far as it is mobile *(ens mobile in quantum mobile)*
>> metaphysics—mobile being in so far as it is existing *(ens mobile in quantum existens)*
>
> Later in inquiry
>> philosophy of nature—mobile being in so far as it is mobile *(ens mobile in quantum mobile)*
>> metaphysics—being in so far as it is being *(ens in quantum ens)*.

Since the philosophy of nature treats of principles which themselves are remote principles of existence, it is clear that the problems of the philosophy of nature may also be studied by the metaphysician. But then either these problems have themselves been transposed to a higher key, treated from the perspective of existence itself (motion and change being now seen as the way to and from existence), or the metaphysician is no longer speaking on the purely metaphysical level.

Although metaphysics can proceed by its own unaided light to the Cause of being for all things, nevertheless it can be considerably aided by the explicit study of the philosophy of nature. For metaphysical terms can in fact only be understood through reference to the sensible and mobile world, the clear understanding of which is the concern of the philosophy of nature.

E. THE DISTINCTION OF THE PHILOSOPHY OF NATURE FROM PHYSICAL SCIENCE

We now come to the exposition of the distinction of the philosophy of nature from physical science in the light of the Thomist tradition concerning the distinction of sciences from Cajetan to Maritain. Unfortunately, it will be necessary to engage in some highly technical and abstract discussions ; these manifest the subtlety of scholastic analysis.

Many maintain that the philosophy of nature is only a continuation of natural science,[1] while others make natural science to be a dialectical continuation of the philosophy of nature.[2] Still others emphasize the practical element of the natural sciences, reducing them in great part to art.[3] But it is clear to many that these sciences have a pronounced speculative aspect as well. For in these sciences there is more than an attempt to control ; there is also a desire to know, to contemplate nature's activity.[4] It is this speculative aspect which concerns us here. If speculative science is distinguished by reason of its object, as was said earlier, our question can be posed as follows : Is there an object of speculation in physical science altogether distinct from the object of the philosophy of nature ?

It does not appear that St. Thomas Aquinas has clearly developed within his system all the principles for such a distinction. But this should occasion no surprise. The special physical sciences either did not exist or were not cultivated in separation from the philosophy of nature in ancient and medieval times.[5] When, through what has been termed a

1. E. WHITTAKER, *Space and Spirit* (London, 1946).
2. KANE-ASHLEY-CORCORAN-NOGAR, *Science in Synthesis* (River Forest, Ill., 1952).
3. V. E. SMITH, *Philosophical Physics* (New York, 1950), pp. 162-169.
4. See, for example, EDDINGTON, *The Nature of the Physical World*, pp. XVI-XVII.
5. MARITAIN, *La Philosophie de la Nature*, p. 87. Even the "mathematicized" sciences remained in close proximity to the philosophy of nature for the ancient thinkers.

"tragic misunderstanding",[1] these sciences completely broke away, in the sixteenth and seventeenth centuries, from the traditional philosophy of nature, their intrinsic independence of the philosophy of nature gradually became manifest. But it was not until the twentieth century that the ground of this distinction in terms of "object" became clear to at least some Thomists. Jacques Maritain, in his *Les Degrés du Savoir*,[2] and later in his *La Philosophie de la Nature*,[3] drew from the Thomist tradition as represented by Cardinal Cajetan and John of St. Thomas principles which he considered adequate to account for a difference of *object* in the "ontological" and "empiriological" disciplines.

We shall examine the doctrine of Cajetan, then supplement it with the teaching of John of St. Thomas, and finally see the application by Maritain to the distinction of the philosophy of nature from natural science.

The doctrine of Cajetan was developed in order to clarify the nature of theology : to make clear the distinction between the knowledge of the blessed, the knowledge of faith, and the knowledge of the theologian. It was supposedly just a clarification of the doctrine of St. Thomas, but whether there is adequate evidence for Cajetan's distinctions in St. Thomas himself is a question which need not concern us here.

While St. Thomas insisted that the speculative sciences were to be distinguished according to their distinct formal objects, as we have seen above, Cajetan further elaborates this notion of formal object[4] by distinguishing two kinds of formal object, one of the thing itself, the other of the thing as known.

> ... note that there is a twofold formal determination of the object in a science : one is of the object *as a thing*, the other of the object *as an object;* or one as *which (quae)*, the other as

1. *Ibid.*, p. 38.
2. Paris, 1932. Pp. 43-134, 265-415.
3. Pp. 70-132.
4. Cajetan's "formal determination of the object" *(ratio formalis obiecti)* can be rendered equally well by our expression, "formal object."

under which (sub qua). The formal determination of the object as a thing, or as *which*, is the determination of the thing (the object) which first terminates the act of the habit, and from which flow the passions of that subject, and which is the middle term in the first demonstration ; as entity in metaphysics, quantity in mathematics, and mobility in natural philosophy. But the formal determination of the object as an object, or as *under which*, is a definite immateriality, or a definite manner of abstracting and defining : that is to say, without all matter in metaphysics, with intelligible matter only in mathematics, and with sensible matter, but not *this* matter, in natural philosophy. [1]

What Cajetan calls the *ratio formalis obiecti ut res* (the formal determination of the object *as a thing*) is therefore a formal determination of the reality precisely as referred to the reality itself, as found in reality.   But the *ratio formalis obiecti ut obiectum* (the formal determination of the object *as an object*) is a formal determination of the reality *insofar as it falls into the intellect*, a determination which consequently has an intentional character and is a medium of knowledge. This latter formal determination is, therefore, in the last analysis, the determinant of what is known *to the extent that it is known*, of the object of knowledge in its precise character as object.   It does not matter how intelligible the object *as a thing* is ; our knowledge of it is limited by the nature of the object *as object*.   Our knowledge is conditioned by the content of the intentional species as well as by the intelligible content of reality.   Thus the formal determination of the

---

1. CAJETAN, *Commentaria in Summam Theologicam S. Thomae Aquinatis*, in editioni Leonina (Rome, 1888), IV. In I, q. 1, a. 3, number III : "... nota duplicem esse rationem formalem obiecti in scientia : alteram obiecti ut *res*, alteram obiecti ut *obiectum;* vel alteram ut *quae*, alteram ut *sub qua*. Ratio formalis obiecti ut res, seu *quae*, est ratio rei obiectae quae primo terminat actum illius habitus, et ex qua fluunt passiones illius subiecti, et quae est medium in prima demonstratione ; ut entitas in metaphysica, quantitas in mathematica, et mobilitas in naturali.   Ratio autem formalis obiecti ut obiectum, vel *sub qua*, est immaterialitas talis, seu talis modus abstrahendi et definiendi : puta sine omni materia in metaphysica, cum materia intelligibili tantum in mathematica, et cum materia sensibili, non tamen hac, in naturali."

object as an object is the true immediate formal principle of the differentiation of sciences.[1] This is to be qualified later, however, by John of St. Thomas.

That this distinction between the two kinds of formal objects is justified is seen from the diversity of the logical and ontological orders, of the order of speculation and the order of being.[2] The conditions of the two orders are not the same. Furthermore, although these two formal objects are sometimes convertible (equivalent, though always distinct), at times, Cajetan tells us, they are not convertible. When the formal determination of the object as an object is an adequate representation of the formal determination of the object as a thing, then the two are convertible. But if the former should not adequately represent the latter, then the two are not convertible.[3] Such an inadequate representation would be

1. *Ibid.*, number V : "Habet igitur obiectum scientiae duplicem rationem formalem : alteram quidditativam sibi ut res est ; alteram denominativam sui simpliciter, quidditativam autem sibi ut est sub genere scibilis ; quod est esse sub genere obiecti, quoniam scibile species est obiecti. Et ideo dictum est quod altera est obiecti ut obiectum est. Et quoniam, quemadmodum sensus distinguitur secundum distinctionem sensibilis ut sic, ita scientia dividitur secundum divisionem scibilis ut sic ; ita quod ubi est una species specialissima scibilis, ibi oportet esse unam tantum speciem scientiae, quemadmodum etiam in sensu et sensibili accidit ; et ubi plures differentiae scibilis ut sic reperiuntur, diversas oportet scientiae species ponere : et si his adiunxeris quod differentiae scibilis ut sic, sunt ipsae rationes formales obiecti scibilis ut obiectum est : de necessitate sequitur quod unitas et diversitas specifica scientiarum attendantur penes unitatem et diversitatem rationum formalium obiectorum ut obiecta sunt ; vel, quod idem est, rationum formalium *sub quibus* res sciuntur."

2. *Ibid.*, number IV : "... quoniam sensus dicitur dividi secundum divisionem sensibilis inquantum sensibile : ita obiectum scientiae est in genere entis et in genere speculabilis, ita quod haec duo genera aliis et aliis differentiis propriis dividuntur in proprias species."

3. *Ibid.*, number IX : "... illa propositio, scilicet : *ratio formalis obiecti ut res, et ratio eius ut obiectum, sunt convertibiles* etc., verissima est, sane intellecta, scilicet de ratione formali obiecti ut sic *adaequata* rationi formali rei. Secus autem est de ratione formali obiecti ut obiectum *inadaequata* rationi formali obiecti ut res (se contingit aliquod obiectum habere rationem inadaequatam) : quoniam inadaequatam non oportet converti cum ratione rei ; sed inferre quidem illam, et non necessario inferri ab illa. Sic autem est in proposito."

traceable to a defect in the intellectual power rather than to the object itself.[1] For the object as object is naturally a representation in the intellect of the object as thing ; *per se* it represents the object in its reality. But *per accidens*, because of the special character of the human intellect, it may represent this object in an incomplete, inadequate manner. This presents the possibility of having more than one specifically distinct formal determination of the object as object corresponding to one same formal determination of the object in reality itself.

A concrete case in which the two formal objects are not convertible is seen in theology, for Cajetan. Corresponding to the unity of the formal determination of the object as a thing, which is deity, is a generic unity of the formal determination of the object as an object, the divine light.[2] But because of the character of the human intellect and the free choice of God, theological knowledge is communicated to us through three *specific* kinds of "divine light". Thus, as Cajetan says, God can be considered in his deity with the aid of the light of glory, the light of revelation, or the light of faith. Corresponding to each of these is a *specifically* distinct theological knowledge.[3]

John of St. Thomas, supposing both the doctrine of St. Thomas Aquinas and that of Cajetan,[4] asks a further question. "What is that formal determination which specifi-

1. *Ibid.*, number XI : "Posset quoque dici quod ratio formalis obiecti dupliciter assignatur : scilicet ex parte obiecti, et haec convertibiliter se habet ad rationem rei ; vel ex parte defectivae potentiae, et haec non convertitur, sed infert rationem formalem rei, et non infertur ab illa."

2. *Ibid.*, number IX : "Quia deitati respondet una tantum ratio formalis adaequata obiecti ut obiectum est, et haec est lumen divinum : sed illa ratio formalis non est una specie, sed genere."

3. *Ibid.:* "... et dividitur in lumen divinum *evidens*, et lumen divinum *revelans* (abstrahendo ab evidentia et inevidentia), et lumen divinum *inevidens*. Et primum est ratio *sub qua* theologiae beatorum, secundum nostrae, tertium fidei. Et propterea, cum unitate rationis formalis obiecti ut res, stat diversitas specifica rationum formalium obiecti illius et obiectum ; et consequenter diversitas specifica habituum."

4. *Cursus Philosophicus*, I, Part II, Question XXVII, Article I, pp. 818b 1-819a 18.

cally constitutes the object as the object of a science and
makes it to differ from another object in its specific determination ?"[1] Starting with the formal determination under
which *(ratio formalis sub qua)* or formal determination of
the object as an object of Cajetan, John of St. Thomas proceeds
to determine precisely what this is. He first points out, and
here he is deeper than Cajetan's account, that this *ratio formalis
sub qua* can be taken in two ways. It may be taken as in
the knowable object *(ex parte rei cognoscibilis)*, in which
case it is the ultimate formal determination, under which
the other determinations are rendered attainable by the
intellect ; this really coincides with the ultimate formal determination of the object as a thing.[2] But it may also be taken
as in the intellect *(ex parte potentiae)*, in which case it is the
light or actuality by which the power is rendered ordered and
actuated for such an object.[3] It is this latter which must be
still further investigated in order to understand the diversification of sciences.

But one more preliminary remark must first be made. The
object of science *(obiectum scibile)*, for John of St. Thomas,
is a complex whole consisting of a subject about which some
property is demonstrated. This demonstration requires a
middle term, a definition. Hence it is the specific *mode of
defining* which will determine the specific mode of knowing
the object scientifically.[4] This is the *ratio formalis sub qua
ex parte potentiae.* Ideally then there should be a distinct

1. *Ibid.*, p. 819a 19-25 : "Quare in praesenti ad hoc devolvitur fere tota diffi-
cultas, ut investigemus, quae sit illa ratio formalis, quae specifice constituit
obiectum in ratione obiecti scientiae et facit ab alio differre in ipsa ratione
specifica."

2. *Ibid.*, p. 819a 49 - b 5 : "... ex parte obiecti cognoscibilis consideratur
formalitas, quae attingitur, et ratio ultima formalis, sub qua ceterae red-
duntur attingibiles, quae coincidere solet cum ipsa ratione quae ultima;"

3. *Ibid.*, p. 819b 5-10 : "... ex parte potentiae correspondet ratio formalis
sub qua attingendi obiectum, quod est ipsum lumen seu actualitas, qua
potentia redditur ordinata et actuata ad tale obiectum."

4. *Ibid.*, 819b 33-38 : "... et ita definitiones, quae se habent ut principia
seu media demonstrandi passiones, debent habere rationem determinandi
scibilitatem talis obiecti illati illuminando illud."

science for every specific essence, if each were known adequately. But since we do not possess such adequate knowledge, we may know many specific natures through one science and one same specific nature through many sciences. Therefore it still remains necessary to show precisely how sciences receive their unity and their diversity. [1] What diversity or unity in the mode of defining is directly responsible for the diversity or unity of scientific knowledge ?

John of St. Thomas first excludes the opinion of those who would make the specific unity and diversity of science to depend on the unity or diversity of the principal subject of science, [2] that about which the science seeks to learn, to demonstrate its causes and passions. [3] This view would not explain how the same subject may be studied by many sciences, as God is studied by both theology and metaphysics. [4] It is not sufficient here to say that there are diverse definitions of the subject for the diverse sciences, for it is still necessary to explain in what this diverse mode of definition consists. [5] This is the precise point which we seek to explain. Moreover, there is a further difficulty ; for quite diverse subjects, each with its own definition, may be treated in the same science. How is such diversity to be unified in one science ? [6] Our problem is not solved ; it is only posed more clearly.

---

1. *Ibid.*, pp. 819b 38 - 820a 10 : "Unde si quaelibet quidditas adaequate et secundum quod est in se cognosceretur, unaquaeque fundaret distinctam scientiam ab alia respectu suarum passionum, sicut probabile est distingui scientiam infusam in Christo secundum distinctionem specierum repraesentantium quidditates, ut significat D. Thomas 3. p. q. 11. art. 6.

Nunc autem cum intellectus sit unitivus et praecisivus nec quamlibet naturam intelligat, ut est adaequate in se, sed coordinat et coniungit cum alia, et e contra unam et eandem rem diversis modis intelligit, contingit diversas naturas pertinere ad eandem scientiam et eandem naturam in diversis scientiis considerari, et sic oportet assignare aliquam rationem, qua plures naturae uniantur in eadem scientia, vel diversas, quibus diversimode considerentur a diversis."

2. *Ibid.*, p. 820a 14 - b 2.
3. St. Thomas Aquinas, Prooemium *In XII Libros Metaphysicorum*.
4. John of St. Thomas, *op. cti.*, p. 821a 4-13.
5. *Ibid.*, p. 821a 14-32.
6. *Ibid.*, p. 821a 33-44.

Speaking still in a general way, John of St. Thomas next establishes that the differentiation of sciences must be traceable to the degree of immateriality or abstraction from matter found in the definitions of the science.[1] This position has already been seen in St. Thomas in the preceding section of this chapter. John of St. Thomas, however, makes some clarifications which we should note.

First he points out that the degree of abstraction spoken of is not to be taken merely in the *subjective* sense of the abstractive act of the intellect ; this would result in a vicious circle where the abstracting sciences would be differentiated by the diverse objects abstracted (by the definitions) while these diverse objects abstracted would be differentiated by the diverse abstracting sciences. Rather, here abstraction should be understood to mean "objective abstractibility" *(abstrahibilitas obiectiva)*, the foundation in the object itself for definitions of diverse immateriality.[2]

Secondly, he points out that the subjective act of abstraction here is not a total abstraction *(abstractio totalis)*, resulting in the abstraction of a universal whole from the singular ; this abstraction must take place in every science. But here there is rather question of a formal abstraction *(abstractio formalis)*, which abstracts formal determinations of varying immateriality.[3] Such formal determination is the true "objective light"

1. *Ibid.*, p. 822a 22-28 : "Generaliter loquendo unitas et distinctio scientiarum in esse scibilis sumitur ex diversa immaterialitate et abstractione, prout primo invenitur in principiis seu mediis demonstrandi et inde derivatur ad illuminandas diverso modo conclusiones."

2. *Ibid.*, p. 822a 34 - b 4 : "Et notandum est, quod non sumimus hic abstractionem pro actu intellectus abstrahente neque pro denominatione extrinseca ex illo consecuta ; sic enim esset circulus, quia diversa scientia abstrahens sumeretur ex diverso obiecto abstracto et denominato a scientia, et diversum scibile ex diversa scientia abstrahente. Sed sumitur abstractio pro abstrahibilitate obiectiva, quatenus in obiecto est fundamentum ad diversam immaterialitatem terminandam et repraesentandam."

3. *Ibid.*, p. 822b 4-17 : "Et non loquimur de abstractione *totali*, quae abstrahit aliquid ut praedicabile ab inferioribus ; sic enim ista abstractio est communis conditio scientiarum, quae non agunt de singularibus, sed de universalibus. Sed loquimur de abstractione *formali*, quae abstrahit rationes formales a materialibus seu potentialibus, et sic constituit seu fundat intelli-

which illumines the conclusions of science. According to its diversity there will be a diversity of sciences. [1]

With this he concludes : "The ultimate species of sciences is not derived from the material diversity of objects in real existence, but from the *diverse grade of immateriality* which is acquired through abstraction,..." [2] It is not enough to consider merely the degree of abstraction *from* matter to determine the distinction of sciences. Abstraction and science must begin with separation from matter as a point of departure *(terminus a quo)*; but they terminate in actuality as a point of arrival *(terminus ad quem)*. This it is which fully consti-tutes the object of science as an object of science. Hence it is from this point of arrival of abstraction that the ultimate specification of science must be taken. [3] The degree of sepa-

gibilitatem. Et secundum quod magis vel minus receditur a materia et mate-rialibus conditionibus, redditur aliquid diverso modo intelligibile;..."

1. *Ibid.*, p. 823b 33 - 824a 9 : "Ex quo apparet verissimum esse, quod unitas et distinctio scientiarum sumitur ex diversitate mediorum seu prin-cipiorum, per quae fit illuminatio scientifica. Rursus vero diversitas medio-rum seu principiorum ex diverso modo definiendi seu intelligendi desumi debet, quae diversitas intelligendi, sive sit in definitionibus et causis sive in effectibus, ad diversam immaterialitatem debet reduci, secundum quam res intelligitur. Quae immaterialitas primo debet inveniri in principiis, ut inde deducatur ad conclusiones, quia scientifica est. Et quia haec principia sic intellecta illuminare dicuntur conclusiones, sic etiam potest dici, quod diver-sitas scientiarum sumitur ex diverso lumine, non quidem se ex parte poten-tiae, quod est habitus ipse seu scientia specifica, sed ex parte principiorum, quae sunt lumen obiectivum determinans ad scientifice probandum conclu-siones."

Ibid., p. 829a 29-31 : "Ex abstractione enim formali sumitur ratio scibili-tatis, non ex abstractione totali."

2. *Ibid.*, p. 824a 10-14 : "Species atoma scientiarum non sumitur ex diversitate materiali obiectorum in esse rei, sed ex diverso gradu immate-rialitatis, quae per abstractionem acquiritur."

3. *Ibid.*, p. 825b 22-35 : "Quare cum specificatio atoma scientiarum sit ultima ratio scibilitatis, quae non est amplius divisibilis, oportet, quod si ratio formalis scibilitatis sumitur ex immaterialitate, ultima et specifica sumatur determinate ex termino ad quem talis abstractionis, in quo ultimo sistit et determinatur abstractio. Ergo non ex sola segregatione a materia, prout consideratur terminus a quo abstractionis, sed in ultima determinatione immaterialitatis specifica et determinata ratio scibilitatis consistet."

Ibid., p. 825a 24-30 : "Quare non solum sumitur ratio formalis et specifica scientiarum ex recessu a materia, sed ex accessu ad determinatum gradum

ration from matter merely locates the science in one of three genera. It is the degree of actuality attained in its definitions which ultimately specifies each science.

Thus the diversity in the mode of defining, from which follows the specific diversity of sciences, is a diversity in the degree of actuality possessed intentionally by the knower and not merely a diversity in the degree to which this definition is "separated" from matter. The real distinction of substance, quantity, and quality is not by itself alone responsible for the distinction of sciences. Beyond this distinction, the mere conceivability, at the same *generic* level of science, of actual determinations which do not as conceived explicitly include some other determinations—even though none of these determinations be completely distinct from the others in its ontological reality—provides a foundation for a more specific distinction of sciences.

Thus, for John of St. Thomas, medicine is distinct from the philosophy of nature, not because the actuality which medicine knows is completely distinct from the actuality which the philosophy of nature knows, but rather because that of medicine can be conceived without explicitly conceiving that of the philosophy of nature, and that of the philosophy of nature without that of medicine. [1]

It would appear that there has been a genuine development of this doctrine of the differentiation of the sciences from St. Thomas through Cajetan to John of St. Thomas. Whether this is only by way of making more explicit what St. Thomas himself really meant or by way of genuine innovation need not concern us here. What is of concern to us is that Jacques Maritain took the doctrine of John of St. Thomas and Cajetan and applied it to the modern problem of differentiating the

immaterialitatis, quo obiectum aliquod determinate deputatur et redditur intelligibile;"

1. *Cursus Philosophicus*, II, Part I, Question I, Article II, p. 19a 36-44: "Nam medicina licet formaliter non agat de corpore naturali, quatenus ens mobile est in communi vel in speciali, agit tamen de corpore naturali ut sanabili, quae sanitas licet per aliquem motum acquiratur, non tamen formaliter ratio motus, sed ordo ad sanitatem attenditur,..."

philosophy of nature from natural science. We must now see how this was done. We shall use as our source Maritain's *La Philosophie de la Nature*.

Maritain first explains his terminology ; this is not the same as that of Cajetan and John of St. Thomas, but it represents basically the same doctrine. The formal determination of the object as a thing (*ratio formalis obiecti ut res* or *ratio formalis quae*) is called by Maritain the *appel d'intelligibilité*, [1] which has been translated in the English edition as "intelligibility-appeal". He retains the term "material object", [2] as meaning simply the reality which is studied. The material object under a special formal perspective, or as having some particular intelligibility-appeal, is called the *sphère d'intelligibilité fondamentale*, [3] or "sphere of fundamental intelligibility". The formal determination of the object as an object (*ratio formalis obiecti ut obiectum* or *ratio formalis sub qua*) is called by Maritain the *lumière objective*, [4] or "objective light".

When the intelligibility-appeal of the reality has, of itself and anterior to any peculiar mode of conceptualization, already a specifying force for the distinction of sciences, Maritain will speak of an "intelligibility-appeal of first determination". [5] This is the case with continuous and discrete quantity (which respectively specify geometry and arithmetic, if these are understood in a non-formalist sense), according to Maritain. When the intelligibility-appeal of the reality, in itself and anterior to its conceptualization by the intellect, is capable of producing only a generic distinction of science (yet to be further specified), as we saw above concerning deity *(deitas)*, the objective light must produce the further specification of the object as object. Here the reality itself does not have *real* distinctions corresponding to the distinctions of the ob-

---

1. *La Philosophie de la Nature*, p. 119.
2. *Ibid.*, p. 120.
3. *Ibid.*, p. 120.
4. *Ibid.*, p. 121.
5. *Ibid.*, p. 126.

jective light ; but the diversity of the objective light in the
intellect *(ex parte potentiae)* makes us nevertheless to see in
diverse ways what is really one and the same. [1] These diverse
aspects of the real, uncovered in the same generic intelligibility-
appeal through diverse objective lights are called by Maritain
"intelligibility-appeals of second determination". [2] This distinction of intelligibility-appeals of first and second determination corresponds to the distinction of John of St. Thomas
between the formal determination of the object as a thing
(ratio formalis quae) and the formal determination of the
object as an object, but as grounded in reality *(ratio formalis
sub qua ex parte rei cognoscibilis)*. The intelligibility-appeal
of second determination therefore is to be equated, in Maritain,
with the objective light on the side of the object *(du côté de
l'objet)*. [3]

Maritain applies these technical distinctions in the meaning
of object to the philosophy of nature and natural science, the
latter of which he has subdivided into "empirioschematic" and
"empiriometric" science. [4] The empirioschematic, or non-
mathematical, [5] sciences have the same sphere of fundamental
intelligibility as the philosophy of nature, namely, being as
mobile. [6] But the objective light [7] of the philosophy of nature,
its characteristic mode of defining, tends toward intelligible
being. [8] It seeks to know the nature or essence of mobile
being. This mode of defining does not allow us to grasp
adequately the detail of phenomena produced by the almost
infinitely complex interplay of these natures in the universe. [9]
There is need then for another objective light, which will lead

1. *Ibid.*, p. 127.
2. *Ibid.*, p. 126.
3. *Ibid.*, p. 121, n. 1.
4. *Ibid.*, pp. 127-132.
5. *Ibid.*, p. 128.
6. *Ibid.*, p. 128.
7. Note that here we are speaking of the objective light, or *ratio formalis
sub qua, ex parte potentiae* and not *ex parte rei cognoscibilis*. Below we shall
use this other meaning as well, as will be seen from the context.
8. *Ibid.*, pp. 128-129.
9. *Ibid.*, p. 128.

the intellect into mobile being precisely in its observable interaction, in its manifestation or appearance in the field of operation, in its phenomenality.[1] Here the knowledge of the intelligible essence is forsaken, but this is so only in order to obtain a more thorough intellectual understanding of the sensible manifestation itself. The mode of definition here is referred to by Maritain as the method of defining through the operation of the senses *(modus definiendi per operationem sensus)*.[2]

To this objective light corresponds, on the side of the reality, an intelligibility-appeal of second determination, which we may call "phenomenality". The phenomena are, of course, not at all separated from the things themselves. They represent only one aspect of the intelligibility-appeal of first determination in the sphere of fundamental intelligibility seen at the first level of abstraction. But this sphere is viewed, in such natural science, in a special way through the *modus definiendi per operationem sensus*.[3]

Thus the formal object of empirioschematic science, taken generically, will be being in so far as it is mobile *(ens secundum quod mobile)*. But more specifically it is "being in so far as it is mobile, under its determination of phenomenality, that is, as defined through the operation of the senses" *(ens secundum quod mobile sub ratione phaenomenalitatis, idest sub modo definiendi per operationem sensus)*.[4]

On the other hand, empiriometric, or mathematical,[5] science of the mobile universe is no longer concerned precisely with motion. Its concern is with mobile being, but with its measurement, its quantity, rather than with its motion (all the while we must recognize that the measurement is of quantitative aspects *of motion*). Thus the intelligibility-appeal, and consequently the sphere of fundamental intelli-

1. *Ibid.*, p. 129.
2. *Ibid.*, p. 129.
3. *Ibid.*, p. 129.
4. *Ibid.*, p. 129.
5. *Ibid.*, p. 130.

gibility itself, is here different from that of the philosophy of nature. It is *quantity*, as in mathematics.[1]

Such science (as, for example, physics) is clearly *about* the mobile universe ; somehow it terminates in mobile being. But nevertheless it is also mathematical. We may say that it is materially concerned with mobility and formally with quantity.[2] Therefore, it deserves the title of "intermediate science".[3] Its sphere of fundamental intelligibility may be termed "mobile being under its determination of quantity" *(ens mobile sub ratione quantitatis)*.[4]

However, the objective light of empiriometric science is distinct from that of mathematics[5] as well as from that of the philosophy of nature. The mode of definition in empiriometric science is "through measurements which the operation of the senses enables us to make" *(par les mesures que l'opération du sens permet d'effectuer)*.[6]

Thus the specific formal object of this science is "mobile being under its determination of detailed measurable phenomenality, that is, as defined by measurements which the operation of the senses enables us to make" *(Ens mobile sub ratione phaenomenalitatis particulatim mensurabilis, idest, sub modo definiendi per mensurationes per operationem sensus permissas)*.[7]

Maritain expresses the object of "empiriological" science (empirioschematic science and empiriometric science taken together) in the formula, "mobile being in so far as it is mobile or in so far as it is quantified, as defined through the operation

1. *Ibid.*

2. *Ibid.*

3. For the notion of an intermediate science, see :

St. Thomas Aquinas : *Summ. Theol.*, I, q. 1, a. 2 ; II-II, q. 9, a. 2, ad 3 ; *In II Phys.*, lect. 3, nn. 336-339 ; lect. 11, n. 477 ; *In De Trinitate*, q. 5, a. 1, ad 5, a. 3, ad 6.

Maritain : *Réflexions sur l'Intelligence*, p. 286 ; *Les Degrés du Savoir*, p. 84; *La Philosophie de la Nature*, pp. 33-38, 97-108.

4. MARITAIN, *La Philosophie de la Nature*, p. 130.

5. The objective light of mathematics does not refer to the operation of the senses, but rather of the imagination.

6. MARITAIN, *La Philosophie de la Nature*, p. 131.

7. *Ibid.*

of the senses" *(ens mobile secundum quod mobile aut secundum quod quantum, sub modo definiendi per operationem sensus).* [1]

On the other hand, as was indicated above, the mode of definition of the philosophy of nature is entirely different. The intelligibility-appeal in the philosophy of nature is mobility ; the sphere of fundamental intelligibility is mobile being in so far as it is mobile. The objective light, or mode of definition, is ontological—we seek to know the intelligible essence or nature. This distinguishes the philosophy of nature from both the empirioschematic and the empiriometric sciences. Maritain defines the object of the philosophy of nature as being in so far as it is mobile, as defined through intelligible quiddity (and not through the operation of the senses), or under an ontological light [*ens secundum quod mobile, sub modo definiendi per intelligibilem quidditatem (et non per operationem sensus), seu sub lumine ontologico*]. [2]

But it is still necessary to explain in further detail what these two modes of defining mean for Maritain : the "ontological" and the "empiriological".

Maritain points out that, because material things appear to us as a "sensible flux stabilized by an idea", it is possible to know them in two ways. Our concepts may have reference either to the nature—the intelligible essence—or to the very sensible flux itself. They may lead us deeper into the being or they may "group together" and "order" the sensible flux without penetrating into the being. Thus the first kind of concept can be said to resolve into intelligible being, while the second kind resolves into the observable; [3] from this we call the two types of conceptualization respectively "ontological" and "empiriological" analysis. [4]

This does not mean that ontological analysis proceeds in independence of the senses ; on the contrary all that we know of the intelligible nature is attained in some way through the

1. *Ibid.*
2. *Ibid.*, pp. 131-132.
3. *Ibid.*, pp. 70-71.
4. *Ibid.*, p. 71.

medium of the senses. But ontological analysis does not intrinsically and directly refer to sensation as its object ; its reference to sensation is only extrinsic. [1]

Similarly, empiriological analysis cannot proceed without any reference whatsoever to intelligible being. We are always abstractly visualizing intelligible natures, whenever we contemplate material being. But empiriological analysis has only oblique reference to this intelligible being. Its direct concern is with the immediately sensible (as a secondary intelligible), with the operational manifestation of the (primary) intelligible in sensible form. [2]

Ontological analysis leaves the sensible manifestations behind as quickly as possible, although they are the necessary foundation, to fasten onto the essence. Empiriological analysis constantly resists the natural impulse of the intellect toward intelligible being in order to achieve a detailed intellectual grasp of the sensible manifestations themselves. Empiriological concepts therefore of necessity designate ultimately only *possibilities for observation*, just as the essences known in ontological analysis are possibilities for being and operation. There is thus some analogy between the role of the concept of an essence in the philosophy of nature and the role of the empiriological concept in physics ; but they tend in opposite directions. [3]

The difference between these two modes of analysis and definition is summarized briefly by Maritain :

> Empiriological analysis... bears on sensible being, but above all as observable or measurable. [4]
> ... ontological analysis, at the first degree of abstraction, likewise bears on sensible being, but above all as intelligible. [5]

1. *Ibid.*, pp. 70-71, 75-76.
2. *Ibid.*, pp. 71, 74-75.
3. *Ibid.*, pp. 72-73.
4. *Ibid.*, p. 75.
5. *Ibid.*, p. 83.

Elsewhere, Maritain names the knowledge arising from ontological analysis *dianoetic*[1] knowledge, while that arising from empiriological analysis is called *perinoetic*[2] knowledge.

F. PROBLEM AND MODE OF PROCEDURE

This doctrine of Maritain thus enables us to distinguish the philosophy of nature from physics (as an empiriometric science) according to their diverse objects. In the succeeding chapters, I hope to elaborate and confirm this doctrine through an analysis of the methods of intellectual visualization employed in these two sciences.

It will be necessary, first, to explain the general meaning of intellectual visualization and of the data to which it is said to refer. Next, we will examine the peculiar methods of visualization found in the philosophy of nature and in physical science. Following this examination of the methods of knowledge, we may then pass to a precise consideration of the *objects* of this knowledge.

1. *Les Degrés du Savoir*, pp. 399-415.
2. *Ibid.*

CHAPTER II

DATA

A. GENERAL CONSIDERATIONS

Since our only direct access to the physical universe by way of knowledge is through sensation, it is clear that for every science[1] of the physical universe there will be some pertinent sense-data. We shall call these simply "data". Such sciences thus have two components : an intelligible content and data to which this intelligible content is in some way intimately related. These two components are in fact always found together, even from the very beginning. But in order to analyze the "method" or "way to truth" of such science, it is helpful at the beginning to distinguish the two components from each other.

We shall consider in this chapter the mere concrete data themselves, before we turn in later chapters to the abstractive visualization of the intelligible content.

This contrast between the data and the intelligible content is recognized in the traditional dichotomy between the sensible and the intelligible, the division between Plato's not-beings and true beings, the distinction between the individual "event" or "instance" and the universal "nature". At this point we are not concerned with the unification of these two components both of reality and of knowledge. Here, we isolate the data in themselves for our study.

As was said above, our only direct contact with the physical universe by knowledge is through the senses. The data

---

1. This is not intended to definitively settle the case in favor of Maritain's position. I speak of more than one science of nature in the sense of Chapter I, A-B. This does not *necessarily* imply the autonomy of each of these, as it is maintained by Maritain. We shall discuss the "autonomy" of these sciences in chapter five.

may be regarded as the "manifestation" of the universe to us, or as its "appearance" in our knowledge. Here, being and knowledge become one ; the sense in act is the sensible thing itself in act.[1] Appropriately then, the data can be termed the *"phenomena"* (what appear).[2] Any natural intellectual knowledge of this universe must begin with the phenomena ; what cannot be seen (or demonstrated through what is seen) in and through the phenomena must remain unknowable to us.

But it should be clear that, whatever may be seen in and through the phenomena by the intellect, the phenomena in themselves, precisely as manifestations of reality in sensation, are characterized by unique individuality and by the absence of all necessary connection with other phenomena.[3] Let us read the words of David Hume :

> Suppose a person, though endowed with the strongest faculties of reason and reflection, to be brought on a sudden into this world ; he would, indeed, immediately observe a continual succession of objects and one event following another, but he would not be able to discover anything further. He would not at first, by any reasoning, be able to reach the idea of cause and effect, since the particular powers by which all natural operations are performed never appear to the senses ; nor is it reasonable to conclude, merely because one event in one instance precedes another, that therefore the one is the cause, the other the effect. The conjunction may be arbitrary and casual. There may be

---

1. ARISTOTLE, *De Anima*, Book III, chapter 8, 431b 23 ; ST. THOMAS AQUINAS, *Summ. Theol.*, I, q. 14, a. 2, c.

2. MARITAIN, *Les Degrés du Savoir*, p. 155, n. 1.

3. But there is an empirical connection to be found, a spatio-temporal collocation is seen, to which we can apply the word *thing*, albeit in a weaker sense than when it is penetrated under the light of the intellect. Cf. MARITAIN, *Les Degrés du Savoir*, p. 184 : "Qu'on pousse plus loin l'analyse correcte du contenu immédiat de la connaissance : on constatera, dans l'ordre lui-même de la connaissance sensitive, que le contenu d'une perception du sens n'est pas seulement telle qualité sensible ou telle stimulation, mais bien, — pour autant que nous pouvons décrire au terme d'intelligence ce qui appartient à un plan de connaissance non intellectuelle — *quelque chose* qui nous envahi comme un champ extensif d'une nuance sensori-affective déterminée, et sollicite ainsi notre motricité."

no reason to infer the existence of one from the appearance of the other : and, in a word, such a person without more experience could never employ his conjecture or reasoning concerning any matter of fact or be assured of anything beyond what was immediately present to his memory or senses. [1]

In any science of the physical world, then, data or phenomena must be considered. But we are confronted with an inexhaustible infinity of phenomena. Which are relevant to the particular science in question ? First we shall seek to find out in a general way which are the relevant phenomena in the philosophy of nature and in physics. Then we shall attempt to state determinate criteria of relevancy for phenomena with respect to these two sciences.

B. RELEVANT DATA IN THE PHILOSOPHY OF NATURE

The philosophy of nature seeks a universal understanding of *all* the data, and yet necessarily contents itself with considering only a very small portion of the data. All the flux of sensation, the total manifestation of the physical universe, is of interest to the philosophy of nature ; none of it is to be left out. The philosophy of nature, as we have seen, seeks the ontological causes for all this flux and manifestation ; it sees in its intelligible light that it is all the manifestation of *motion*.

But in order to discover the *general* ontological causes of the phenomena, the philosophy of nature need not consider every kind of phenomenon. Because of the abstractive and generalizing power of the human intellect, some phenomena may stand for all as manifesting these general intelligible principles to us.

For example, consider Aristotle's investigation of the general ontological principles of motion in the *Physics*. [2] He

---

1. D. Hume, *An Inquiry Concerning Human Understanding* (New York, 1955), p. 56.
2. *Alpha Physicorum*, 7, 189b 30 - 191a 22.

intends to discuss "becoming in its widest sense" ;[1] the discussion will thus concern all phenomena, through all of which the intellect can discern motion (see chapter III). Yet throughout his analysis he considers in detail only two concrete cases of becoming, that of a "musical man" and that of a "bronze statue". However, the treatment is obviously general. He is speaking primarily of the becoming, not of a "musical man" or of a "bronze statue", but of informed matter in general. His conclusions are valid for all becoming of any kind.

Thus the philosophy of nature, in its first investigations of the still quite general causes of motion, does not require a complex and detailed knowledge of the phenomena. A few simple phenomena would be far more desirable than many complex phenomena. Indeed, an overwhelming manifold of detail might be far more of an impediment than a help. Reduction to unity through abstractive generalization is rendered difficult, if not impossible, by the presence of great multiplicity.

In the investigation of phenomena in a more detailed way, as we shall see later, we cannot clearly "see", or abstractly visualize, the operative causes. Here the philosophy of nature cannot even partially accomplish its task unaided. It is necessary for physics and the other special natural sciences to continue in their own ways the effort to reduce the multiplicity of phenomena to intelligible unity and thus to provide matter in some degree fit for further consideration by the philosophy of nature. [2]

To conclude, the philosophy of nature considers *all* the phenomena, at first generically with a few simple phenomena "standing for" all the rest, and later specific kinds of phenomena, but this with the aid of the special natural sciences. These natural sciences all taken together examine *all* the phenomena in the special ways proper to these sciences. We shall consider below the particular case of physics.

We shall not be very much concerned in this essay with the

---

1. *Alpha Physicorum*, 7, 189b 30.

2. J. MARITAIN, "Philosophy and the Unity of the Sciences", *Proceedings of the American Catholic Philosophical Association*, XXVII (1953), 42-54.

consideration of specific phenomena by the philosophy of nature aided by the special sciences. Rather we will treat the philosophy of nature mainly in its generic study of motion ; and we will treat physics as following the line of development dictated by its own nature independently of its assumption under the higher objectives of the philosophy of nature. [1]

C. RELEVANT DATA IN PHYSICS

We have indicated that the special natural sciences, taken together, examine all the detail of phenomena. This is in a way also true of physics taken alone. But there is one restriction to bear in mind concerning physics. *It is absolutely necessary for the data to yield a number.* However complex and detailed the phenomenon, at least one number must arise from and be included in the phenomenal context. But seldom, if ever, do we discover such numbers in naturally occurring events. We must obtain them by the process of measurement, and through the use of measuring instruments —which therefore themselves contribute a part of the total phenomenon.

Thus the total phenomenon of physics is generally in principle more complex than the phenomenon of the philosophy of nature ; for the former has an artificial component. This is as true when the measurement is made in the course of observation of a naturally occurring event, e. g. in the measurement of an eclipse of the sun or moon, as it is when we measure in an experimental situation, e. g. in the measurement of spectral lines. For both cases require the use of a measuring instrument, which itself adds to the complexity of the total phenomenon. We generally attempt to make the natural component of the phenomenon as simple as possible, even at the price of greatly multiplying the complexity of the artificial component. This is well and good—we already understand the artificial component, at least in so far as it is artificial.

1. The last three paragraphs anticipate in part the conclusions of chapters four and five.

It would seem then that we are introducing intellectual direction and intelligibility into the very constitution of the phenomenon of physics. But this intellectual direction, while indeed present in the techniques of experiment and measurement, remains extrinsic to the phenomenon as such. The phenomenon itself is still nothing more than a complex of sense-data, arising in accordance with the laws of nature in the given situation.

Yet we must be very careful not to confuse the total experimental context with the phenomenon. The total experimental context always includes, in the experimenter, a component of theoretical interpretation in addition to the phenomenal component.[1] For example, the "scattering" experiments of Rutherford[2] were made in the framework of the atomic theory of J. J. Thomson[3] in order to deepen this theory itself.[4] The phenomenon here is not the scattering of alpha and beta particles by atomic nuclei but rather the appearance of points of light on a scintillation screen,[5] or still better the manifestation of points of light on a background which we call zinc sulfide. This is, of course, something of an oversimplification. The phenomenon is really more complex, including measurable distances and other aspects of the experimental apparatus ; but the point should be clear.

But a further difficulty arises, since we say that a *number* is included in the phenomenon. How can this be so, since we restrict the phenomenon to the level of sense-data ? It is

1. Indeed, in addition to both of these components, there is also found some degree of knowledge of substances, causality, and other transphenomenal reality. This knowledge, however implicit it be, influences (and is indeed needed by) the experimenter in many ways ; but as such it does not pertain to the structure of physics, as we shall see later on.

2. E. RUTHERFORD, "The Scattering of A and B Particles by Matter and the Structure of the Atom", *The London, Edinburgh and Dublin Philosophical Magazine and Journal of Science*, 6th series, 21 (1911), pp. 669-688.

3. RUTHERFORD, *ibid.*, p. 670.

4. *Ibid.*

5. *Ibid.*, p. 674 : "... we see from this equation that the number of A particles (scintillations) per unit area of zinc sulphide screen at a given distance..."

necessary to distinguish between numerable number and numbering number (*numerus numerabilis* and *numerus numerans*). Numbering number is number disengaged from the things which must concretely embody it. Clearly, we know this kind of number by some kind of intellectual knowledge. But numerable number is only the objective quantity which is capable of being measured. We may call the relative position of a pointer on a scale, the proportion of an extended physical line to some physical measuring standard, or the ticks of a Geiger counter, numerable number. It is such a quantitative character which must appear in any phenomenon of interest to physics. The intellectual expression of this quantitative character, now involving a numbering number, does not pertain to the phenomenon itself.

Thus the phenomenon of physics is a set of sense-data including at least one numerable number. It is apparent that physics, although its interest may be primarily centered on that number, still presupposes a qualitative diversity of data. In a purely quantitative world, the number would be without a meaningful context ; indeed in such a world we could never even know the number itself, since quantitative relationships are revealed to us only in the context of qualitative diversities —e. g. of color.

Physics then demands as its material a measurable phenomenon ; its first interest is to measure it in some way. This phenomenon is complex, possessing both natural and artificial components. At least one of its components must be determinately quantitative in character ; for it becomes measurable insofar as one quantitative component can be the measure of another, or insofar as "counting" can take place.

Let us see an example from physics itself. Consider one of the "scintillation" experiments of Rutherford.[1] What were the characteristics of the phenomenon ? Lord Rutherford outlines them for us, at least in part.

1. E. RUTHERFORD, "Collision of A Particles with Light Atoms, Part IV. An Anomalous Effect in Nitrogen", *The London, Edinburgh and Dublin Philosophical Magazine and Journal of Science*, 6th series, 37 (1919), p. 581.

The apparatus employed to study these "natural" scintillations is the same as that described in paper I. The intense source of radium C was placed inside a metal box about 3 cm. from the end, and an opening in the end of the box was covered with a silver plate of stopping power equal to about 6 cm. of air. The zinc sulphide screen was mounted outside, about 1 mm. distant from the silver plate, to admit of the introduction of absorbing foils between them. The whole apparatus was placed in a strong magnetic field to deflect the beta rays. The variation in the number of these "natural" scintillations with absorption in terms of cms. of air is shown above in fig. 1, curve A. In this case, the air in the box was exhausted and absorbing foils of aluminum were used. When dried oxygen or carbon dioxide was admitted into the vessel, the number of scintillations diminished to about the amount to be expected from the stopping power of the column of gas. [1]

Obviously, the phenomenon contains a wealth of qualitative data, named by "radium C", "metal box", "silver plate", "zinc sulphide screen", etc. But all of these, though necessary, are not themselves enough to make the experiment contribute to the progress of physics. The scintillations must be *counted* under various arrangements of phenomena, and these arrangements themselves are specified primarily in the *quantitative terms* of distance (or some equivalent), specific numerical characteristics of the elements, etc.

The *quantitative* data yielded under determinate qualitative and quantitative conditions permitted Rutherford to construct his explicative hypothesis. These quantitative data are the norm, the final court of appeal, for the hypothesis. It is precisely these quantitative data which the hypothesis seeks to explain.

From the results so far obtained it is difficult to avoid the conclusion that the long-range atoms arising from collision of alpha particles with nitrogen are not nitrogen atoms but probably atoms of hydrogen, or atoms of mass 2. If this be the case, we

1. *Ibid.*, p. 581.

must conclude that the nitrogen atom is disintegrated under the intense forces developed in a close collision with a swift alpha particle, and that the hydrogen atom which is liberated formed a constituent part of the nitrogen nucleus. We have drawn attention in paper III, to the rather surprising observation that the range of the nitrogen atoms in air is about the same as the oxygen atoms, although we should expect a difference of about 19 per cent. If in collisions which give rise to swift nitrogen atoms, the hydrogen is at the same time disrupted, such a difference might be accounted for, for the energy is then shared between two systems. [1]

As Kelvin declared in the late nineteenth century, [2] and as de Broglie, [3] Eddington, [4] and many others have repeated in this century, physics is concerned with the measurable ; what can in no way be measured is of no interest to physics.

D. CRITERIA OF RELEVANCY

What then makes a phenomenon relevant to the philosophy of nature, considered as a generic study of nature, or to physics ? First, what are the criteria of the relevancy of phenomena to the general philosophy of nature ?

Clearly, *simplicity* is of the utmost importance. We cannot easily disengage the intelligible principles from complex phenomena—there are limitations to the multiplicity which the intellect can overcome. Yet every phenomenon, even in the general philosophy of nature, must also have a *minimum degree of complexity*. Unless an opposition of sameness to otherness is discerned by the intellect in or through the phenomenon, there will be no reason to consider the phenomenon

1. *Ibid.*, p. 586.

2. Cited in R. A. MILLIKAN, *Electrons (+ and —), Protons, Photons, Neutrons, and Cosmic Rays* (Chicago, 1935), p. 4.

3. L. DE BROGLIE, *Physics and Microphysics*, trans. M. Davidson (New York, 1955), p. 78.

4. EDDINGTON, *The Nature of the Physical World*, p. XI.

further. But such an opposition requires a certain complexity in the phenomenon itself.

Similarly, *commonness of occurrence* is also important, not in itself but for us. The general philosophy of nature should take as examples phenomena which are accessible to all without difficulty, lest this science become esoteric. Thus it should consider examples like those of Aristotle, who considers such elementary examples as a man learning to play a musical instrument, or the making of a statue, in order to understand the intelligible principles of any motion whatsoever. [1]

Since the phenomenon produced in an experimental situation is very complex, and also uncommon, the general philosophy of nature should not, as a rule, concern itself with experimental situations, but rather with simple *natural* occurrences. Thus it could consider falling bodies, but not in the complex experimental situation of the inclined planes and viscous liquids of Galileo. Its effort is to consider the phenomenon in a primitive simplicity.

Lastly, the phenomena must be truly phenomena, that is, they must have in themselves *no logical component of theoretical "interpretation"*. All "theories" must be put aside. The structures of the quantum theory, for example, must not be in any way considered as entering into the constitution of the phenomenon itself.

So much for the philosophy of nature. What now are the criteria of the relevancy of phenomena to physics ?

We have already seen the necessity of the phenomenon containing a *measurable*, a numerable number. Indeed, ordinarily there must really be at least *two* such measurables, one the measuring instrument, the other the measured. The process of measurement itself in such a case is a comparison of these two.

But we have already seen that the phenomenon must contain more than the mere measurables ; these occur in a *qualitative context*. The phenomenon of physics must be a

---

1. *Alpha Physicorum*, 7.

rather *complex* phenomenon, containing at times a considerable number of quantitative and qualitative elements.

We have also seen that determinately measurement-yielding phenomena rarely occur in nature ; it is necessary to use *instruments* and to create *artificial phenomenal complexes* (experimental situations) to obtain phenomena relevant to physics.

As was also pointed out above, *the natural component of the phenomenon should always be as simple as possible.* Complexity is to be placed in the artificial component rather than allowed in the natural component. We can understand the complexity of the artificial component, precisely because it is artificial. But complexity in the natural component, over which we do not have control, lessens the possibility of "understanding" the total phenomenon.

Thus, we will always break down natural phenomena into the simplest possible elements for investigation through experimentation. We will remove perturbing factors such as variations of temperature, irregular movement of the whole system, etc., as far as possible. This raises the most serious problem as to just how we limit a complex phenomenon and distinguish it from other phenomena. How do we decide what is relevant *to a given complex phenomenon* and which consequently should be included in its description. Although the first limitations suggest themselves more or less naturally (see Appendix II), usually the complexity of a physical phenomenon must be finally limited according to the prescriptions of our theoretical physical interpretations of phenomena.

But even measurable phenomena are of no great use to physics unless *substantially the same collocations and structures of phenomena* either remain or recur, with *variations primarily in the quantitative elements*, variations *expressible in terms of mathematical law.* This will be considered in more detail later.

Finally, these phenomena must be *public;* they must be observable to anyone who is given the proper tools.

CHAPTER III

ABSTRACTIVE VISUALIZATION IN GENERAL

A. THE NATURE OF ABSTRACTIVE VISUALIZATION

In addition to our seeing of the concrete sense data, we also possess another knowledge of the real, entirely different in kind. This second is opposed to the first in that its objects are abstract and universal (at least with regard to their manner of presence in the intellect) while the first is concerned only with the concrete and individual as concrete and individual. These two knowledges, must, however, always be viewed as essential complements in human knowledge. Though distinct, we never find them in isolation from each other. There is a genuine "seeing" in both cases. Compare the understanding of "dog" with the seeing of the particular group of appearances which embody and manifest the content of the idea here and now in the instance of "Fido". We may refer to such understanding as abstractive visualization. [1]

Abstractive visualization must be clearly distinguished from reasoning. The former brings the intellect into a state of rest in the contemplated object, while the latter is the very movement of the intellect (according to intelligible laws) from contemplation already achieved to rest in new objects of contemplation. Thus reasoning may be said to have abstractive visualization as its beginning and end ; the purpose of reasoning is ultimately only to deepen our abstractive visualization of reality. Reasoning supplies, to the extent that it can, for the imperfection of our intellect, which gradually moves from

---

1. The term "abstractive visualization" is used by Maritain (*La Philosophie de la Nature*, p. 12) to designate the abstract intellectual vision of the intelligible content of reality. Maritain's usage of this term seems to apply only to conceptualization ; our usage is wider as will be seen below.

potency to act and, at the beginning, visualizes things in only an obscure way.

Thus, abstractive visualization is the fundamental act of the human intellect. It is the act by which the intellect actually attains reality in the way proper to the intellect. It is expressed imperfectly in the concept, more perfectly in the judgment.[1] But it is important to note that both concept and judgment express acts of this kind. It is evident that the term "abstractive visualization" is therefore analogical in its meaning.

Obviously, any scientific knowledge of the physical universe requires, in addition to the data, the abstractive visualization of the intellect. It is only the perfection of this latter that enables us to call science the most perfect knowledge[2] had by men. Here sense knowledge of the fluctuating data lacks the stability and necessity which we attribute to science. It is abstractive visualization which enables us to see the stable intelligible principles which manifest themselves in the data. These intelligible principles are then, in one way or another, the *causes* of the phenomena. Thus we say that science is a "knowledge through causes".[3]

But not all abstractive visualization constitutes a scientific knowledge. Abstractive visualization of some kind is concomitant with all human sense knowledge, but only *stable* and *clear* abstractive visualization possessed *systematically* can constitute science. Clarity is, of course, a relative term— some sciences can achieve greater clarity than others. But the clarity even of the metaphysician or ethician is in obvious contrast to the obscurity of "common sense". We also require a *systematization* of abstractive visualization for science.

---

1. I take judgment here to mean the assent to the perception of the content of the conception *as realized*, and not as the resultant statement about this perception and assent. Whether the intellectual assent is identical with the very act of perception, I do not wish to discuss here.

2. St. Thomas Aquinas, *In I Analyticorum Posteriorum*, lect. 4, number 5: "... scire aliquid est perfecte cognoscere ipsum,..."

3. St. Thomas Aquinas, *Summa Contra Gentes*, Bk. I, c. 94 : "scientia est rei cognitio per propriam causam."

Because we cannot grasp the reality in its intelligible plenitude by a single act, human science requires a multiplicity of acts. But such a multiplicity would not possess the clarity and stability proper to science if it were not ordered into a system with adequate directions (logical rules) for moving from one part of the system to another.

Because of this systematization, the abstractive visualizations of a science are both end and source in the science. We seek to see—this is abstractive visualization. But we also seek to discourse about the entire intelligibility of the object, so far as this is possible—this requires systematization and reasoning. Thus the achieved abstractive visualizations are themselves means by which we can proceed to still further seeing. The problem in science, then, is to attain abstractive visualizations which not only give insight but also are apt for systematization and through which we may move to still further insight.

Immediately therefore the question poses itself, "What kind of abstractive visualization is suitable for scientific knowledge?" In order to determine this it is first necessary to divide the various kinds of abstractive visualization.

B. DIVISION OF ABSTRACTIVE VISUALIZATION

Although we consider both the concept and the judgment as expressions of the abstractive visualization of reality, nevertheless we may divide it by a consideration of concepts alone. The same division will be seen to apply to judgments as well.

To obtain a satisfactory division of concepts or universals,[1] we may turn to the Preface of the Commentary of Cajetan on the *De Ente et Essentia* of St. Thomas Aquinas.[2] Cajetan

---

1. The term universal here should not be understood in the restricted sense of one idea realizable univocally in many things taken distributively, but rather as referring even to ideas which are realizable only analogically.

2. THOMAS DE VIO CAJETAN, *In De Ente et Essentia D. Thomae Aquinatis Commentaria*, ed. P. M.-H. Laurent (Taurini, 1934).

regards the universal as a totality, or rather as including two totalities. The universal may be considered either as a definable whole or as a universal whole ; we would say today that it can be considered either in its intension or in its extension.

As a definable whole, the concept is an expression of the actuality of the thing considered. On the other hand, as a universal whole, it has a certain "realizability" in individuals —a real extension. Clearly, the first totality is prior to the second—there is no realization without an actuality to be realized. But the two totalities are nevertheless distinct ; and we can abstractly visualize the same reality in a variety of ways depending on how we grasp each of these totalities. Cajetan enumerates four kinds of abstractive visualization.

Knowledge of a definable whole may be called *actual* knowledge, since it focuses on the actuality involved. Knowledge of a universal whole may be called *virtual* knowledge, since it focuses on the capacity of this actuality for realization in the world. But both *actual* and *virtual* knowledge may be either *confused* or *distinct*.

Confused actual knowledge is "that by which what is actually found in the object is known without penetration,"[1] that is, "without resolving it into its definitive parts".[2] An essence is intensively grasped, but only in an obscure way. Such knowledge is not compatible with any form of distinct knowledge, either actual or virtual.

Confused virtual knowledge is "that by which the object is known in an imperfect manner with respect to what is virtually contained in it",[3] that is, "without compounding it with its subjective parts[4]".[5]

---

1. *Op. cit.*, q. 1, n. 3, p. 3 : "qua citra penetrationem cognoscitur id quod actualiter in objecto invenitur."
2. *Ibid.*, p. 2 : "qua objectum secundum id quod virtualiter in ipso includitur non perfecte cognoscitur."
3. *Ibid.*, p. 3 : "qua objectum secundum id quod virtualiter in ipso includitur non perfecte cognoscitur."
4. Subjective parts are the individuals in which the universal nature is *subjected*, or realized.
5. *Op. cit.*, p. 2 : "... non componendo ipsum cum partibus subjectivis."

Distinct actual knowledge is "that by which what is actually found in the object is penetrated",[1] that is, "by resolving it into the individual parts of the definition".[2] Confused virtual knowledge is compatible with distinct actual knowledge ; we may know an essence intensively and in a complete manner without knowing its extension in the real world, as with philosophically interpreted (hypothetical) constructs of physics such as the various atomic models of Lewis-Langmuir, Ruther-ford, Bohr, etc.

Distinct virtual knowledge is "that by which an object is penetrated with respect to that which is virtually included in it",[3] that is, "by compounding it with its subjective parts".[4] This knowledge is not compatible with any form of confused knowledge, whether actual or virtual.

These four forms of knowledge, concretely considered, reduce to only three, since virtual knowledge is never found without some kind of actual knowledge, nor can actual knowledge be found without some form of virtual knowledge. We are left with the following possibilities :

(1) confused actual and confused virtual knowledge
(2) distinct actual and confused virtual knowledge
(3) distinct actual and distinct virtual knowledge

These are divisions of conceptual knowledge. But may they be extended to the knowledge of judgment, which we have also included in abstractive visualization ? How may we analyze judgment into intensive and extensive aspects ?

We shall represent judgments in formulas borrowed from the modern logic of terms. Our discussion should, however, be understood to be about the intellectual perception rather than about its mere representation. Can we see diverse aspects in the perception, which may properly be called intensive and extensive ?

1. *Ibid.*, p. 3 : "qua penetratur id quod actualiter in objecto invenitur."
2. *Ibid.*, p. 2 : "... resolvendo ipsum in singulas partes diffinitionis."
3. *Ibid.*, p. 3 : "qua objectum penetratur secundum id quod virtualiter in ipso includitur."
4. *Ibid.*, p. 2 : "... componendo ipsum cum suis partibus subjectivis."

Suppose we consider the judgment, "All men are mortal". Using capital letters for classes taken in intension and small letters for individual-variables, with the usual logical functors, we may symbolize this judgment as follows : (x) : A(x)⊃B(x). This should be read as "For all x, if x is an A (man), then x is a B (mortal)". For x in this case we may substitute any individual.

Consider likewise the judgment, "Peter was the first Pope". Using the same symbolism as above, we have : (∃x) : A(x).B(x). This should be read as, "There is at least one x such that x is an A (a man named Peter) and x is a B (the first Pope).

Or consider again this judgment, "This box in front of me is red". Symbolized it will read : (∃x) : A(x).B(x).C(x). This is to be understood as follows : "There is at least one x such that x is an A (a box), and x is a B (a thing in front of me), and x is a C (a red thing).

It should be clear from these examples that the variable *x* designates in some way the *extension* for which the judgment is intended, while the capital letters and logical functors designate the *intension* or meaning of the judgment. The judgment, then, shows these two aspects of extension and intension just as does the concept. Hence our division of concepts according to the divisions of Cajetan can be taken to apply to judgments as well, therefore to all abstractive visualization.

C. ABSTRACTIVE VISUALIZATION AND SCIENCE

What kind of abstractive visualization is required for scientific knowledge ? We have already pointed out a double aspect in science—it is actual (in Cajetan's sense) knowledge and at the same time it is logically interconnected knowledge. The discourse of reason must supply for the deficiency of our immediate abstractive visualization of things. We tend toward a single abstractive intuition of reality in its intelligible plenitude. But we can only achieve an imperfect substitute through the building of a complex intellectual structure, the "cement" of which consists in logical relations.

In so far as science seeks to see, to gain insight into reality, as clearly as possible, it is necessary for it to obtain *distinct actual knowledge*. The abstractive visualization of science is above all a visualization of actuality, grasped to the most complete degree possible.

But in so far as the separate insights of a science must be brought into a systematic unity of insight as far as possible, they must each be such as to aid in leading us to other insights through discourse. In other words, the abstractive visualization of science must have a relational character. It must not only make us to see, but also at the same time have in itself, as present in the intellect, what tends to lead us beyond itself to other abstractive visualization. This is only to say that it must also be a suitable term in logical reasoning.

What then are the requirements to make a term suitable for use in logical reasoning ? In all logical reasoning, the fundamental concern is not with the immediate intellectual insight itself but rather with the movement of the intellect from one immediate insight to another. Indeed, in purely formal logic, immediate insight is not considered at all (although it is presupposed) ; the movement of the intellect, its discourse, alone matters. Now the characteristics of abstractive visualization flowing from the absolute *actuality* attained are of no consequence with respect to discourse considered in its formal character as discourse. To what other characteristics can we look ?

We have already seen that, besides the intensional aspect of visualization, we can also discern an extensional aspect, an applicability of the actuality in question to the real existing or capable of existing independently of the intellect itself. Moreover, this extensional point of view is of itself relational. The actuality, formerly considered in itself without relation to any other, is now seen as related to a world of individuals. This presents the possibility of linking abstractive visualizations to each other in terms of their extensional relations. The abstract study of the general forms of such linkage was the concern of traditional Aristotelian and scholastic formal logic. [1]

But then, we have found what we are looking for, a quality of abstractive visualizations which enables them to principiate discourse, namely their applicability to the real world of individuals. This applicability should be clearly grasped in a truly scientific visualization ; this visualization should convey, in addition to *distinct actual knowledge*, a *distinct virtual knowledge* as well.

The abstractive visualization of science, then, must always be precise in its content and in its scope. But thisdoes not necessarily require that we see the actual application to all possible individuals, which would be impossible ; it suffices to know the *applicability*.

Yet it should be remembered that science is primarily seeking actuality. It is the actuality attained which characterizes a science. Virtual knowledge presupposes actual knowledge and is only a means of extending our actual knowledge to the whole world of individuals and of leading us to other actual knowledge.

D. ABSTRACTIVE VISUALIZATION IN RELATION TO SENSE DATA

It must be understood that human knowledge is always a composite of abstractive visualization and sense data. Although these two are always distinct they are never separated. We invariably find, in our knowledge of reality, two elements which clearly distinguish themselves one from the other—we find a set of appearances which is extended, com-

1. I do not in any way deny the possibility of other logical relations than the extensional (derived from a consideration of the actuality attained, in so far as it itself is not simply absolute actuality but also relative to other actuality), or their place in the unification of systematic knowledge. But at least the extensional relations are always, in fact, present ; and their consideration here especially aids us in better understanding scientific abstractive visualization.

plex, successive, everchanging ; and we find insight expressed in an idea or set of ideas which is unextended, relatively simple, non-temporal, changeless. The idea somehow gives "form" to the appearances, while the appearances somehow "embody" the idea.

An idea or abstractive visualization of physical reality can be said to *unify* phenomena. It does this in virtue of its meaning, which has a reference to some given group of phenomena. The multiplicity of phenomena which are thus "referred to"[1] by the idea is gathered together into a unity through the idea.

Likewise, the idea may be said to *stabilize* the phenomena. The flux of phenomena as such has in itself no ground of permanence. But the idea provides a nucleus of stability in so far as its content is embodied in the flow of phenomena. The idea contains in itself such a reference to these phenomena as to provide, even in its changelessness, a stable center of change. Thus it both unifies the phenomena and gathers them around itself.

As we should have already seen, it is not just that our scientific abstractive visualization unifies and stabilizes our *knowledge*. Rather, its objective content in some way also seems, at least in many cases, to unify and stabilize *the reality itself*. This requires much closer investigation, however ; we reserve it to the next chapter.

1. This is not to say that the idea means *only* the phenomena. It may mean much more, although its meaning depends in one way or another on these phenomena.

CHAPTER IV

ABSTRACTIVE VISUALIZATION IN THE PHILOSOPHY OF NATURE AND IN PHYSICAL SCIENCE

A. PERINOETIC AND DIANOETIC ABSTRACTIVE VISUALIZATION OF NATURE

At this point it is necessary to return to Maritain's distinction between *perinoetic* (empiriological) knowledge and *dianoetic* (ontological) knowledge.[1] Each of these involves a distinct type of abstractive visualization ; each is related in its own special way to phenomena. We must examine these relations in detail.

Both perinoetic and dianoetic knowledge grasp an intelligibility present to the intellect—both are themselves intellectual. But from this point on, the differences are much more important than the similarities.

Dianoetic visualization enables us to see an intelligibility which is itself transphenomenal. The unification and stabilization of phenomena by this intelligibility, which we noted in the last chapter, is here not only in knowledge but even in the very things themselves. Our vision is, at least obscurely, of the substantial natures, the essences of real existents. We are contemplating, no longer just the manifestations of being, but the being itself.

Maritain explains the nature of dianoetic visualization briefly as follows :

We mean by [dianoetic intellection]..., that mode of intellection in which the intelligible constituent of the thing is objectivated in itself (if not through itself, at least through a sign which manifests it, through a property in the strict sense of the

---

1. See chapter 1.

term). ... this is to designate an intellection which, through the sensible, attains the nature or essence itself. [1]

Maritain emphasizes that we are *not* here in possession of an *immediate intuition of the essence*. We grasp it only through its properties. [2] Since we are not pure spirits, our intellectual grasp of reality can be achieved only in conjunction with the operation of the senses. Only with attention to the manifestations to sense can we form an idea of the essence.

But does this mean that we must first understand the properties in order afterward to understand essences, that the proper object attained primarily and of itself [3] by the human intellect is not the quiddity of material substance ? By no means. It is necessary to distinguish between knowing the quiddity and quidditatively knowing the quiddity. [4] A quidditative knowledge of the quiddity is the distinct actual knowledge which we spoke of in the previous chapter. To merely know of the quiddity in a vague, indistinct way, it is not necessary to know any properties—the intellect confusedly sees quiddities under the natural light of its first principles [5] immediately in the confrontation of sensible being. But in order to attain to a distinct knowledge of the formal structure of the quiddity, it is necessary painstakingly to search out properties and to proceed *a posteriori* to the intelligible constitution of the nature whence they flow.

1. J. MARITAIN, *Les Degrés du Savoir*, p. 401, n. 1 (translation mine).
2. *Ibid.*, pp. 401-402, 405, 409-410.
3. *Summ. Theol.*, I, q. 85, a. 8, c.
4. J. MARITAIN, *Les Degrés du Savoir*, p. 412.
5. ST. THOMAS AQUINAS, *De Veritate*, q. 11, a. 1, c. : Similiter etiam dicendum est de scientiae acquisitione ; quod praeexistunt in nobis quaedam scientiarum semina, scilicet primae conceptiones intellectus, quae statim lumine intellectus agentis cognoscuntur per species a sensibilibus abstractas, sive sint complexa, ut dignitates, sive incomplexa, sicut ratio entis, et unius, et huiusmodi, quae statim intellectus apprehendit. Ex istis autem principiis universalibus omnia principia sequuntur, sicut ex quibusdam rationibus seminalibus. Quando ergo ex istis universalibus cognitionibus mens educitur ut actu cognoscat particularia, quae prius in potentia, et quasi in universali cognoscebantur, tunc aliquis dicitur scientiam acquirere.

Yet, as was said in chapter one, we do not penetrate very far in knowledge of the essential notes of physical reality. In this way of dianoetic knowledge we can attain clearly only the generic aspects of reality, except in the world of man. [1] Whence it follows that we cannot achieve a stable and unified *science* of physical reality in this way on any but a very limited scale.

We are thus confronted with an enormous mass of phenomena for which we can understand no determinate quidditative participations in being as the cause. We know that such natures exist, but we do not know their intrinsic intelligibility with any clarity at all.

But then, how are we to achieve a science of these phenomena ? How to achieve a stable unity of knowledge here, even though we cannot grasp the stable ontological unities ? It is here that we enter into the realm of *perinoetic* knowledge.

The phenomena in themselves lack all necessity and causal connection; this is rather to be found in the existent substantial natures or essences and their properties. Therefore, the abandonment of hope for further dianoetic visualization leaves us with the necessity of superimposing on these phenomena themselves a constructed intelligibility. Thus the intelligible stabilization and unification of phenomena are here finally accomplished from outside the phenomena themselves *(ab extrinseco)*.

The phenomena here are signs of the essence, but signs which hide the essence from our view more than reveal it. [2] Our intellection here terminates primarily in the multiplicity of phenomena themselves rather than in the ontological principles of the phenomena.

Perinoetic abstractive visualization then requires something like a Kantian a priori with respect to the phenomena, in so far as it superimposes on the phenomena a universality and a necessity which they do not have of themselves. [3] How-

1. J. MARITAIN, *Les Degrés du Savoir*, p. 405.
2. *Ibid.*, p. 409.
3. Immanuel KANT, *Critique of Pure Reason*, trans. N. K. Smith (New York, 1950), Introduction II, pp. 43-45.

ever, there are at least three important differences from the Kantian a priori which can readily be seen. Firstly, the phenomenon, as we conceive it for perinoetic knowledge, would already be composed, for Kant, of the sensuous manifold and the a priori forms of space and time. Secondly, the Kantian a priori was a natural apparatus of the human mind ; the perinoetic a priori is, on the contrary, constructed by the human mind. Thirdly, the Kantian a priori originated in complete independence of all experience whatever ; but the perinoetic a priori is constructed of elements the ultimate origin of which is in abstractive visualization of the phenomena (either of sense or of the imagination[1]), and this a priori construction constantly refers to the phenomena so as to assure its suitability as a unifying and stabilizing factor.[2] With these reservations, it might seem just as well to call it an a posteriori ; but we persist in calling it an a priori because, strictly speaking, *it is not imposed on us but rather constructed by us and imposed on the phenomena.*

But a difficulty immediately arises concerning the perinoetic a priori. How are we to unify the phenomena as such with such an extrinsic constructed intelligibility ? Perinoetic intel-

1. We may speak of phenomena properly of the imagination in so far as a quantity disengaged from sensible qualities *appears* to us in the imagination, as we rise to the level of mathematical abstraction. From this point of view, mathematics can be a perinoetic knowledge. All mathematical constructions have direct or indirect reference ultimately to such phenomena of the imagination, except in so far as such constructions pass beyond the frontiers of mathematics itself and into the domain of logic, or, on the other hand, into the philosophy of quantity or the philosophy of nature. Mathematical constructions in physics are here regarded as perinoetic, however, *primarily* because, as used in physics, they refer to the sensible phenomena, indeed are only considered in physics in so far as they ultimately refer to the sensible phenomena. For diverse meanings of "mathematics" see Appendix I.

2. This necessity of constant reference to the phenomena does not necessarily settle the question as to the presence of some arbitrarily chosen (or spontaneously and naturally arrived at) structure antecedent to all detailed experience of sensible phenomena, as a general framework for all physical knowledge. This kind of framework has been noted by A. S. Eddington (*The Philosophy of Physical Science*, Cambridge, 1949) and denied by Max Born (*Experiment and Theory in Physics*, Cambridge, 1943). See Appendix II, section B, for some observations.

lection terminates in the phenomena themselves and does not explicitly consider the transphenomenal intelligible grounds of the phenomena. What is the intelligible object through which the knowledge through the perinoetic a priori immediately terminates in the phenomena ? We have said that this intelligible object must ultimately be immanent in the phenomena. But how are we to see the universal and necessary in the particular and contingent phenomena ?

It must be understood that *the phenomena themselves may be known in a universal and necessary way.* [1] We have intellectual knowledge, not only of the substantial natures or essences of things but also of their accidents and manifestations. We need not know the substantial nature to understand what "red" is, or other sensory qualities, or extension and number (as founded in the sensible or imaginable). We can understand various forms of phenomenal measurement (by comparison of extensions or by counting) without knowing natures. That is, we need not know these natures *quidditatively.* It still remains necessary always to grasp at least the *confused* notion of substantial quiddity, without which these accidents and manifestations could not be understood in any way whatever, since accidents include substance in their definition. But it is not the clearly defined and disengaged substance of the philosophy of nature which is here studied ; rather it is a vaguely known substratum, which might even be easily confused (as has happened) with the phenomena themselves or with pure geometrical extension or with the "space" of physics.

---

1. Indeed, one may strongly suggest that all intellection regarding transphenomenal natures in fact presupposes, grounds itself upon, a first—often merely implicit—intellection regarding phenomena. The inquiring intellect drives toward knowledge of the nature ; but it cannot ask the question : "what is it ?" unless first there is already given an *intellectual* awareness of the thing in its phenomenality. This awareness, as we said, is often implicit. In perinoetic intellection the tendency of the intellect to ask further questions, about the nature, is resisted ; as a consequence all that we have is intellectual awareness of the thing in its phenomenality, now become *explicit* since it is no longer immediately left behind by the inquiring intellect—this is perinoetic knowledge.

This knowledge, an intellectual grasp of the phenomenon in its phenomenality, provides us with elements for our first perinoetic constructions, elements themselves endowed with universality and necessity and consequently capable of contributing to complex constructions also possessing universality and necessity. This intellectual grasp of the phenomenon in its phenomenality appears to be what Maritain primarily intends by the term, *perinoetic knowledge*.[1] This much must be derived from nature ; the complex perinoetic constructions are in great part an artificial work of the intellect and imagination. The mathematics often employed in perinoetic construction in physics is not, of course, derived from perinoetic knowledge of the sensible phenomena, but from the constructive activity of the intellect in the properly mathematical sphere of the "praeter-real",[2] (and grounded in perinoetic knowledge of imaginable quantity[3]).

It is clear then that we are confronted with at least six possible types of abstractive visualization in our scientific knowledge of nature. We may grasp an intelligibility abstracted from nature or an intelligibility which is constructed and imposed on nature. We may call the first an a posteriori intelligibility and the second an a priori intelligibility. An a posteriori intelligibility is imposed on us and gives us an (abstractly) intuitive grasp of reality, but the a priori intelligibility is constructed by us and *as such* does not give us an intuitive knowledge of reality. But the possibility remains (which we shall see more of later) of a

1. MARITAIN, *Les Degrés du Savoir*, pp. 405-406.

2. On this conception of mathematics, see *op. cit.*, pp. 92-93, 279-284.

3. The reader familiar with the thought of Maritain will note that my conception of perinoetic mathematical knowledge, as distinguished from any philosophical knowledge of quantity, is not to be found explicitly in Maritain. For him, mathematics deals, not with phenomenal quantity, but with real quantity (transphenomenal)—abstracted, however, from the real conditions of existence, transferred to the domain of the "praeter-real". I agree that there is a transference to the "praeter-real" domain; but the quantity thus transferred is *phenomenal* quantity and not transphenomenal quantity. Despite this difference, however, I believe I am simply proceeding along a line suggested, even if not completely followed up, by Maritain.

knowledge which is both a priori and a posteriori, from different points of view.

The a posteriori intelligibility may be a transphenomenal nature or it may be intra-phenomenal (that is, it may be the intelligibility of the phenomenon in its very phenomenality). The first of these is the object of what Maritain calls *dianoetic* visualization, the second the object of *perinoetic* visualization. The a priori intelligibility may be constructed from elements abstracted either dianoetically or perinoetically. If the first, it will constitute a construct of the Aristotelian type ; if the second, it will be like the physical models of modern physics. If the elements of such perinoetic a priori construction are drawn, not from the understanding of sensible phenomena, but from the mathematical domain, we will then have a mathematical model. The conditions under which such a mathematical model becomes useful in our knowledge of physical nature are considered in section C of this chapter. There also will be noted the way in which one may even pass beyond the mathematical model to a purely *logical* model. We shall call the perinoetic a priori construct (whether a "physical" or a "mathematical" model), with the qualifications made above, a "Kantian a priori".

Our division therefore may be as follows :

> Scientific abstractive visualization of nature
> > a posteriori
> > > transphenomenal (dianoetic)
> > > intraphenomenal (perinoetic)
> > a priori
> > > Aristotelian (dianoetic)
> > > "Kantian" (perinoetic)
> > > > physical
> > > > mathematical
> > mixed a priori and a posteriori [1]

---

1. We have not yet discussed this mixed knowledge, but it is included by way of anticipation.

The meaning of these divisions will become more clear in the course of the discussion. Maritain's division seems to correspond mainly to our division of a posteriori abstractive visualization. But it is necessary to introduce the a priori visualization as well, in order to give a complete account of our knowledge of nature, as will be seen below. Maritain himself has recognized the importance of our "Kantian a priori" in modern science. [1]

But note that any construction, however complex, of perinoetic knowledge of the physical world must refer totally to observable and measurable elements of this world. "Unobservables," such as mathematical equations, which may enter into these constructions, have noetic significance only in reference to the observables which they (noetically) unify and stabilize and predict. And, of course, there can be no question at all of explicit and direct dianoetic significance here, since our concern is solely with the phenomena. If there is any such ontological significance *per accidens*, it can only be discerned as such in the light of higher dianoetic knowledge.

To summarize, the universal and necessary constructions of perinoetic knowledge serve to unify and stabilize the particular and contingent phenomena from outside the phenomena themselves. These universal constructions are related to the particular phenomena through the medium of elements of construction which are themselves direct abstract visualizations of phenomena in their phenomenality, though necessarily including—obliquely and implicitly—an obscure awareness of substance (not clearly disengaged from the phenomena themselves).

But up to now we have been proceeding in a more or less a priori manner. It is now necessary to come to an examination of the philosophy of nature and of physics to ascertain whether these types of knowledge we have been discussing may actually be found there.

---

1. MARITAIN, *Les Degrés du Savoir*, p. 104.

B. ABSTRACTIVE VISUALIZATION IN THE PHILOSOPHY OF NATURE

1. *The most general level of the philosophy of nature*

What kind of abstractive visualization is employed in the
philosophy of nature ?   We first consider the simplest visualizations and then proceed to the more complex.   We may
consider, for example, Aristotle's definition of motion in the
third book of the *Physics*,[1] as "the act of a being in potency,
so far as it is in potency".

Clearly, this definition of motion requires a complex abstractive visualization.   But its elements, "primitive terms" of
the philosophy of nature, are here very simple.   They have
not yet been clarified and expressed in the complex concepts
of the developing and developed philosophy of nature.

What are these primitive concepts ?   They are two : "being
in potency" *(dynamei ontos)* and "act" *(entelecheia)*.   The
meaning of potency and act here is clarified in the following
remarks by St. Thomas Aquinas in his Commentary on this
text :[2]

> Therefore it should be considered that one thing is only in
> act, another only in potency, and another midway between pure
> potency and perfect act.   Therefore what only is in potency is
> not yet moved ; but what is already in perfect act is not being
> moved, but is already moved.   Therefore that is being moved
> which is midway between pure potency and act, which is partly
> in potency and partly in act as is evident in alteration.   For
> when water is only potentially hot, it is not yet moved ; but when
> it is already heated, the motion of heating has terminated.   But
> when it already participates partially but imperfectly in heat,
> then it is being moved to become hot.   For what becomes hot
> little by little shares in heat more and more.

Thus potency is the capacity of any being to acquire a
perfection, its act.   Act and potency are correlative terms.
The block of marble is in potency to becoming a statue, the

---

1. *Gamma Physicorum*, 2, 201a 10-11.
2. *In III Physicorum*, lect. 2, n. 559.

form of the statue being the act. The child has the potency to become an adult. Potency and act are to be found throughout the domain of being ; they divide every genus of being. [1]

But these conceptions of potency and act express an attempt, preliminary and yet to be deepened, at insight into the very nature of reality itself. These are not mere logical categories for Aristotle. He regards them as principles of real *being*. Nor are they considered to be only hypothetical principles ; the manner of speaking is everywhere categorical. How does he come to them ?

Before answering this question, we may point out that act and potency here are not taken in their full metaphysical amplitude and significance. Rather, they are here synonymous with form and matter (*morphē* and *hylē*). In the philosophy of nature we do not get beyond the levels of form and matter ; act and potency are found concretized, as it were, in form and matter. Thus our question really reduces to asking how one may arrive at the conceptions of matter and form and what is their significance in the philosophy of nature.

It is in the first book of the *Physics*, especially in chapter seven, that Aristotle arrives at these conceptions. The procedure has already been touched upon earlier in this essay. Let us summarize briefly the procedure of Aristotle.

The problem of chapter seven is to understand the principles of becoming *(genesis)* in its widest sense (in the physical universe). The analysis is as follows. In all becoming there is something new and the original lack of this something new. Moreover, there must be an "underlying subject", something which remains in the course of the becoming. This is seen to be true both in substantial and accidental becoming. The "underlying subject" is named "matter", while the "something new" is named "form". The "lack" is called "privation".

A preliminary abstractive visualization of "becoming" is required for this process. The transobjective reality [2] of

---

1. *In III Physicorum*, lect. 1, n. 548.

2. I use this term "transobjective" in the sense of Maritain (*Les Degrés du Savoir*, p. 410).

"*subjects which become*" is evident in immediate insight. Even so subjectivist a thinker as Sir Arthur Eddington is prepared to grant the reality (in a non-subjectivist sense) of "becoming".[1]

Likewise, Meyerson regards this most evident fact of becoming as an insuperable obstacle to all "scientific" attempts to reduce reality to an identity, although this assertion must be understood within the framework of his "realist" epistemology of science.[2]

Given this preliminary, somewhat obscure abstractive visualization of being becoming other than itself, the philosopher of nature clearly disengages the components of such being, the intrinsic principles of becoming. The vaguely known complex resolves into clearly known components : matter, form, and privation. Of course, these components clearly seen provide us with a clearer understanding of the complex itself, and of the being which has become ; but this does not concern us at the present moment.

What concerns us here is the character of these components. They are seen to be *real* (ontological) principles of *real* (ontological) becoming and being. We are not merely constructing plausible hypotheses to "save the appearances" of becoming. Rather there is immediate insight into the transphenomenal intelligible principles of the phenomena. But this is what we earlier called "dianoetic abstractive visualization". The same dianoetic character is to be found, at least in tendency, not merely in these simple abstractive visualizations of the most universal principles of becoming in the physical universe but also in the understanding of all particular realizations of these principles in the diverse genera, species, differences, properties, and accidents of mobile being.

But questions immediately pose themselves. How do we proceed in the complex abstractive visualizations of the more developed philosophy of nature ? What is the noetic status of such complex abstractive visualizations ? Do they perhaps

---

1. *The Nature of the Physical World*, pp. 94-95.
2. E. MEYERSON, *Identity and Reality*, trans. Kate Loewenberg (London, 1930), p. 265 ; *ibid.*, p. 278.

lose their dianoetic character with increasing particularization, as appeared to be the case for Aristotle when he passed from the *Physics* to the treatise *On the Heavens?* To these questions we may now turn.

2. *The intermediate level of the philosophy of nature*

We may consider first an example at an intermediate level. After discussing the general principles of becoming in its widest sense, Aristotle proceeds to investigate further the general characteristics of mobile being. He makes a definition of motion, and shows that motion is a property of mobile being.[1] He examines the notion of the infinite, since motion is continuous "and the infinite presents itself first in the continuous".[2]

Next, Aristotle begins to explain what "place" is. This is necessary for a general understanding of mobile being "both because all suppose that things which exist are some-where (the non-existent is nowhere—where is the goat-stag or the sphinx ?), and because 'motion' in its most general and primary sense is change of place, which we call 'locomotion'."[3] We shall briefly review his discussion here to determine what kind of knowledge he reaches. Is it still dianoetic or has Aristotle by now lapsed into only an illusion that he is still talking about the real world ?

We are not asking whether Aristotle's definition of place has any special contribution to make to modern physical science. We only seek to discover its contribution to our dianoetic knowledge of mobile being.

First, let us examine the position of the problem. The *existence* of place is regarded by Aristotle as obvious. We

---

1. *Gamma Physicorum*, c. 1-3. See M. A. GLUTZ, *The Manner of Demonstrating in Natural Philosophy* (River Forest, Illinois, 1956), for an explanation of this procedure.

2. *Gamma Physicorum*, 1, 200b 17 (translations are taken from the Ross translation).

3. *Delta Physicorum*, 1, 208a 29-32.

speak of different beings successively occupying the same place.[1] There is not a question here of mere localization in an ideal coordinate system ; the concern is with a characteristic of mobile beings in their proper real existence. Their intrinsic being is considered to require more than a "to be" (SEIN) ; it also has a special "to be there" (DASEIN).

Aristotle further emphasizes the reality of place and of being in place by attributing to them a certain influence on the local motion of mobile being. Bodies are said to have their proper places toward which they tend to move when they are not in them. Moreover, these places ("up and down and the rest of the six directions") are distinct from each other independently of our knowledge ; the distinction is not just relative but absolute.[2] This doctrine of "natural place" is developed in the *De Caelo*. We shall consider it later. Before proceeding further, we should note that this doctrine of "absolute" natural place is in fact a secondary development ; the existence and general definition of place are presupposed by it but need not themselves involve this doctrine.

But supposing that place has some kind of real existence, independently of the consideration of the mind, the question still remains concerning its *nature*. Aristotle raises a series of difficulties concerning place, which are so serious as to impel him again to cast doubt, at least verbally, on the real existence of place.[3] These difficulties all concern the explanation of just *how* place can be said to exist ; from the difficulty of conceiving its nature, Aristotle is led again to say that perhaps it does not exist after all.

Yet it is clear that the doubt of Aristotle here is only rhetorical, for he enters immediately into the question of the nature of place without any further attempt to establish its existence. The difficulties are indeed serious and necessitate a lengthy discussion, but they are only difficulties after all. The evidence for the existence of place is too strong simply to deny.

1. *Delta Physicorum*, 1, 208b 1-8.
2. *Ibid.*, 208b 8-24.
3. *Ibid.*, 209a 29-30.

After ruling out the possibility of place being either matter or form, [1] Aristotle begins his own investigation of its nature by asking what it means to be *in* place. He notes that nothing can be primarily in itself, [2] but rather it needs to be in another. Thus he has further reason to affirm that place is not identical with either of the intrinsic causes, matter or form. [3]

Before coming to the formal definition of place, Aristotle sums up our knowledge of its attributes. It is the first container of that of which it is the place. It is not anything of that of which it is the place. It is neither greater nor smaller than the thing. It is separable from the thing (many bodies may successively occupy the same place). It is, in a general way, natural to some bodies (this attribute need not concern us now). [4]

Concerning the genus of place, it is clear that it must be either the matter, the form, an interval between the edges of two bodies, or one of these edges themselves. The first three are easily excluded. The genus of place is seen to be the "inner edge of the containing body". [5]

But when this containing body is itself in motion, then it is rather to be considered as a vessel than as a place ; for example, the boat moving down a river is not so much a place with respect to what is in it, as a vessel. It is the river which, being as a whole stationary, will provide a place for the boat. [6] Hence the specific difference of place is that it is "immobile".

From this Aristotle concludes to the definition of place as "the innermost motionless boundary of what contains". [7]

The difficulty surrounding the term "motionless" in this definition is readily seen. We do not have evidence of absolute rest in the order of local motion. How then can we define place in such a way as to require such knowledge ? Clearly we know of places even without this absolute knowledge. The distinc-

1. *Delta Physicorum*, 2, 209b 1 - 210a 11.
2. *Ibid.*, 3, 210a 33 - b 8.
3. *Ibid.*, 3, 210b 27-31.
4. *Ibid.*, 4, 210b 32 - 211a 6.
5. *Ibid.*, 211b 5 - 212a 7.
6. *Ibid.*, 212a 7-19.
7. *Ibid.*, 212a 20-21.

tion made by Aristotle between place and vessel must break down.

Aristotle himself did not have this difficulty since he regarded the earth as being at rest at the center of the universe.[1] Consequently, everything at rest with respect to the earth could be regarded as at rest in an absolute sense. St. Thomas Aquinas develops this conception of a knowably motionless place in his distinction between "common place" and "proper place".[2] The outermost celestial sphere (common place) serves to make all place intelligible. Proper place is not primarily so-called from the immediate container but because of its *situs* within the immobile whole. "The whole intelligibility of place in all containers is from the first which contains and locates, that is to say, the heaven."[3]

Thus the Aristotelian definition of place in fact presupposes a doctrine itself evolved from later investigations concerning the detail of mobile being. Because this doctrine is not firmly established, the definition of place that is given here requires some revision. We see here already a tendency away from dianoetic insight toward a "philosophical myth", a doctrine which is dianoetic in tendency but which does not give genuine insight.

Yet we have come to see that "being in place" is an attribute of mobile being quite independently of the consideration of the mind. Clearly, to define this "place" *would* be a contribution to our firmly grounded dianoetic knowledge of mobile being, if only we could accomplish this in independence of any "myths" concerning the detailed structure of the physical universe.

It is not necessary to abandon completely Aristotle's definition. It is only necessary to define place in a completely relative sense by admitting that the "immobility" in question is only relative, thus destroying the clear distinction between a place and a vessel. Indeed, even Aristotle himself recognizes

1. *Beta De Caelo*, c. 14.
2. *In IV Physicorum*, lect. 6, nn. 896-900.
3. *Ibid.*, n. 900.

the intimate relationship between place and vessel when he notes that "as the vessel is transportable place, so place is non-portable vessel". [1]

This relative definition of place is certainly grounded in reality. Even if we were one day to discover a way of knowing absolute place (which seems unlikely), our relative definition would still be valid in its own order. It points out an essential relativity of mobile being to other mobile being ; and it leads us to an understanding of the contiguity of all physical reality, at least of all that we know about. This in turn enables us to see a fundamental unity of the physical world in the sphere of operation.

Thus, in this consideration of place, we are still advancing in dianoetic knowledge of mobile being, still on a very general level but nevertheless dianoetic. The ideal of the philosophy of nature remains such dianoetic knowledge. It would, if possible, extend its insight into all the specific natures of mobile being. [2] Whether it can succeed in this attempt or not, it certainly stands on this very general level as more than the hypothetical science that it has been conceived to be by moderns like Santillana.

> Cosmology is, and is expected to remain, a most conjectural science, for it is safe to say that we shall never know anything about the universe as a whole. Our present position, in fact, is that our acknowledged ignorance about it grows faster than the advance of knowledge, for every time we advance our theory by one logical type, in the language of Bertrand Russell, the structure of the whole complicates itself by several. [3]

3. *The less general level of the philosophy of nature*

But the Aristotelian philosophy of nature, although persisting in its dianoetic *tendency*, fails to attain clear and certain

---

1. *Delta Physicorum*, 4, 212a 14.
2. St. Thomas Aquinas, *In De Sensu et Sensato*, lect. 1, n. 2.
3. Santillana, Historical Introduction to *Dialogue on the Great World Systems*, Galileo Galilei, trans. Santillana (Chicago, 1953), p. xxii.

dianoetic knowledge on any but these more general levels of the intelligibility of mobile being, except in the cases of the generic distinctions of things, and of the specific nature of man. The natures of things do not easily manifest to us their intrinsic intelligibility. We may be said to know generally *that* natures differ from each other. We do not usually know in *what* these differences consist, or just where to draw the line between specifically distinct things.

We see an example of this failure of the Aristotelian philosophy of nature in the *De Caelo*. Let us outline in a summary way the Aristotelian description of the nature and structure of the physical universe and its parts, which is contained chiefly in the first two books of this treatise.

For Aristotle, motion is the key to the knowledge of the fundamental natures of things. A nature, for Aristotle, is the "source or cause of being moved and of being at rest in that to which it belongs primarily, in virtue of itself and not in virtue of a concomitant attribute".[1] Thus from the diversity of motion we can know the diversity of natures and something of what these natures are.

Among material and sensible things we can discern three kinds of simple and natural locomotion : motion upwards in a straight line, motion downwards in a straight line, and circular motion.[2] According to whether bodies have one or the other of the first two motions they are called light or heavy. There are four basic elements instead of two, however ; for, in addition to absolute lightness (possessed by fire) and absolute heaviness (possessed by earth), there is also relative lightness (possessed by air) and relative heaviness (possessed by water).[3] These four elements—earth, water, air, and fire— tend to range themselves around the center of the universe with earth at the center, water on it, air above it, and fire at the outer edge of the sublunary world. Bodies composed of mixtures of these follow the tendency of the predominant element

1. *Beta Physicorum*, 1, 192b 21-23.
2. *Alpha De Caelo*, 2, 268b 14-24 ; 3, 270b 28-31.
3. *Delta De Caelo*, 1, 308a 7-33 ; 4, 311a 15 - 312a 21.

in their composition.[1]   But the sublunary world does not reach a static state since these elements are ever being changed one into another.[2]   All bodies in the sublunary world are composed of these elements and consequently have one or other of the two natural motions upward and downward.[3]

But there also exist bodies which move with a circular motion,[4] a motion of rotation.[5]   These are the spheres of the moon and of the other heavenly bodies. Circular motion has no contrary, while motion downward and motion upward are contrary to each other.[6]   Moreover, circular motion is necessarily primary ; for the perfect is prior to the imperfect, and the circle is perfect while the straight line is not.[7]   Since circular motion is primary, it must be the motion of some simple body, prior to all the terrestrial elements, more perfect than they.[8]   That this motion is natural to the heavenly bodies is seen from its continuity and eternity.[9]

On all these grounds, therefore, we may infer with confidence that there is something beyond the bodies that are about us on this earth, different and separate from them ; and that the superior glory of its nature is proportionate to its distance from this world of ours.[10]

The body moving in a circle cannot move up or down, either naturally or unnaturally.[11]   Since its motion has no contrary, the body has no contrary.[12]   Therefore such a body

1. *Alpha De Caelo*, 3, 269a 1.
2. *Beta De Generatione et Corruptione*, 10, 337a 8-15.
3. *Alpha De Caelo*, 8, 277b 14-24 ; 2, 269a 17-18.
4. *Ibid.*, 2, 268b 14-24 ; 5, 272a 16-17 ; 5, 272b 13-15 ; *Beta De Caelo*, 4, 287a 11-14.
5. *Ibid.*, 9, 278b 28-29 ; *Beta De Caelo*, 4, 287a 11-14.
6. *Ibid.*, 2, 269a 9-18.
7. *Ibid.*, 2, 269a 19-24.
8. *Ibid.*, 2, 269a 23-28.
9. *Ibid.*, 2, 269b 5-8.
10. *Ibid.*, 2, 269b 14-17.
11. *Ibid.*, 3, 269b 31-32.
12. *Ibid.*, 3, 270a 12-22.

is ungenerated, indestructible, and unchangeable except for its constant circular local motion. [1]

Thus, for Aristotle, a radical dichotomy exists between celestial and terrestrial matter, which is made manifest by differences in motion. [2]

The bodies beyond the sublunary world are spheres [3] which, as we have said, move with a rotatory motion. This is most clear in the case of the primary body, which rotates once a day. This body cannot be infinite nor can any other of the heavenly bodies be infinite, since an infinite body could not rotate. [4] Since the universe is not infinite, it must have some figure ; and this figure is that of a sphere. [5]

The circular motion of the celestial bodies is continuous and regular. [6] The first motion (the daily rotation of the sphere of the fixed stars) is one movement, while the other apparent motions are combinations of many circular motions. [7] The celestial bodies observed by us are contiguous with the spheres in which they are, and they are of the same nature as these spheres. [8] There is a large number of such spheres, a number hypothetically determined in astronomy to account for the apparent motions of the celestial bodies. [9]

Given these conceptions regarding the nature of terrestrial and celestial matter, the plan of the universe for Aristotle is as follows. The earth is at the center of the universe, [10] which is also the center for the concentric heavenly spheres ; and all terrestrial matter is found below the moon. Beginning with the moon is the celestial world, with its fifth element in circular motion. The bodies constituted by this element

---

1. *Ibid.*, 3, 270a 12-35.
2. *Ibid.*, 2, 269b 14-17.
3. *Beta De Caelo*, 4, 287a 4-6 ; 11-14.
4. *Alpha De Caelo*, 5, 271b 1 - 273a 6.
5. *Beta De Caelo*, 4, 286b 10 - 287b 21.
6. *Ibid.*, 6, 288a 13 - 289a 10.
7. *Ibid.*, 6, 288a 14-17 ; *Lambda Metaphysicorum*, 8, 1073b 1 - 1074a 31.
8. *Ibid.*, 7-8, 289a 11 - 290b 11.
9. *Lambda Metaphysicorum*, 8, 1073b 1 - 1074a 31.
10. *Beta De Caelo*, 14, 296a 24 - 297a 8.

are a series of spheres which contain the observed heavenly bodies, a series of spheres concentric with the earth and rotating in various directions to account for the observed appearances of the heavens.

This world-view of Aristotle is meant to describe the nature of things. And yet there is nothing in it that would not be rejected today or at least held as suspect. What Aristotle intended to be more detailed science of nature is regarded by us as hardly above the level of the myth of Plato's *Timaeus*. It is a myth constructed with closer attention to the physical world than was given by Plato ; but it is nevertheless a myth. The mistake of Aristotle is understandable. He perfected a philosophical method to an exceedingly high degree and attempted to apply it here in a sphere in which it did not give the desired result—insight into the real transphenomenal intelligible principles of things. We cannot blame him for making the experiment—he was unaware of the extent to which the transphenomenal intelligibility of the physical universe is hidden from us. Indeed, we may profit much from reflection on this failure. Its cause is not so much in the inadequacy of Aristotle as in the inadequacy of the human intellect as such in the face of the physical real.

4. *The limitations of dianoetic knowledge*

In order to grasp the intelligibility of the mobile universe as it is revealed through mobility, it is necessary for us to include matter in our concepts ; for matter is a necessary principle of mobility. And yet, at the same time, the matter of real things is for us a principle of unintelligibility by reason of its indetermination, and a principle of multiplicity. Thus it constitutes an obstacle to the intellect in its movement toward the intelligibility and unity of the mobile universe. We need to abstract from matter, but we are unable to do so completely ; for this would put us outside the sphere of mobile being altogether.

It is necessary to renounce all thought of attaining to the ultimate intelligibility and unity of the individual as such, by a properly philosophical and scientific mode of knowing. This does not deny the possibility of gaining an intellectual knowledge of this individual (in close conjunction with sense knowledge) ; but such knowledge will be too particularized, too immersed in matter, to fit into a systematic structure of knowledge, into a science. We must leave such insight to the poet, to the literary man, in general to the "pre-philosophers", who unveil and present to the philosopher a wealth of insight for him to assimilate to scientific philosophy as best he can. Philosophical knowledge is always *relevant* to the individual, but it cannot completely *include* the individual in all its individuality.

Forsaking the possibility of a scientifically philosophical knowledge of the individual in its individuality, we abstract from individual sensible matter. This abstraction enables us to reach a new level on which multiplicity is considerably diminished and on which we find some objective intelligibility commensurate with our intellects. We are still in the realm of the mobile, in so far as our conceptions still contain matter (common sensible matter) ; thus we can here have philosophical knowledge about the mobile world. This is the level of the philosophy of nature. Here we can understand the principles of becoming, the nature of motion, the necessity of a First Mover, and many other truths concerning the physical universe.

But again, matter (common sensible matter) is also a principle of specific multiplicity and blocks a reduction to complete unity even on this abstract level. It is only in the determinations of matter which are common either to the entire realm of mobile being or to large segments of it that we ourselves can discover sufficient unity and intelligibility to constitute a science. It is possible for us to know of prime matter and substantial form in general ; but the potency of matter is infinite, so that the possible determinations of matter are infinite— thus the full intelligible depths of substantial form are found to be refracted in countless ways through the prism of prime matter. The unity and intelligibility which we found are broken into innumerable fragments. There are far more things in heaven and earth than are dreamed of in the general philosophy of nature.

In our efforts to understand farther the specific natures of the mobile universe, we are all but frustrated by another effect of that which enters into the constitution of all things mobile, namely, contingency. Because we live in a universe permeated by contingency, it is extremely difficult for us to learn of the determinations of matter. For these must be learned through the activities of things, and these activities may well be the effect of a plurality of causes, a plurality which is not known to us exhaustively. This is all ultimately due to the passivity which things possess by reason of their matter, the principle of their finitude. Because of their limitation, these things not only act but also are surrounded by other agents which act on them. And this prevents us from attributing activities to uniquely determined agents or even to uniquely determined pluralities of agents. For we can never know, without a complete knowledge of the entire universe, that any activity is determined uniquely by a particular agent or group of agents. We are speaking here not just of a contingency of the individual, but even of a contingency of the species.

To summarize our discussion of the philosophy of nature, we see that it tends toward knowledge of the transphenomenal real but fails to achieve a scientifically clear and certain grasp of this real except on a level which is still quite general. The mobile universe presents a multiplicity to us which is in itself all reducible to a unity of knowledge ; however, this unity is not known to us but in the unity of the Divine Essence.

What is to be done ? Is it possible now in any way to continue in the proper direction of the philosophy of nature toward the transphenomenal specific natures of things ? Certainly, the ideal of clear and systematic dianoetic *insight* at the less general level cannot be achieved, at least not at this present moment in the history of thought.

5. *A substitute for dianoetic insight into actual reality*

Although it is true that clear dianoetic knowledge is not achieved concerning, for example, the nature of the ninety-two elements and their various compounds, or of light, of electricity, of thermal energy (the ontological counterpart of the scientific conception), nevertheless we do possess an obscure dianoetic knowledge of these things. Through any sensible manifestations we come to know the transphenomenal intelligible principles, however obscure be this knowledge. Such knowledge is on the whole inadequate for science ; confused actual knowledge is compatible only with confused virtual knowledge, while science requires both distinct actual and distinct virtual knowledge, as we noted in chapter three.

Such confused knowledge can be refined and used in idealized intellectual constructions, but this "idealization" does not result in any clearer grasp of the transphenomenal object itself. This process only gives us "ideal" essences, not necessarily corresponding to the "real" essences, since clear vision is lacking. Out of these ideal essences an ideal "world-picture" such as that of the *De Caelo* can be constructed, an ideal picture the constituents of which are ideas dianoetic in *tendency* but not in *termination*.

Since these ideal essences are not imposed on the mind by reality but are rather constructed by the mind itself, albeit from elements themselves imposed on the mind by reality, we may regard them as an *a priori* structure with respect to the real world. This is the *Aristotelian a priori* of which we have spoken earlier in this chapter. In so far as we use this structure as a means of viewing the real world, it may properly be termed *dialectical*,[1] only *tending toward* clear dianoetic insight without actually achieving it with clarity or completeness.

---

1. This is not dialectic in the Aristotelian sense of a knowledge gained through principles simply extraneous to the science, but it has an analogy with that dialectic in so far as it is a knowledge of reality gained through logical entities—these "ideal" essences are constructs ; they exist only in the mind.

Aristotle himself recognized the role of such an *a priori* in, for example, astronomy.[1] Unfortunately, he does not seem to have realized how soon such an *a priori* becomes necessary in the philosophical study of nature proceeding from the more general to the less general.

This dialectical process may be regarded as bearing a certain analogy to the "philosophical myth" of the *Timaeus* concerning the physical world.[2]

But note that such an *a priori* structure, though not "scientific" when considered as a means for understanding the nature of things, since these are seen only obscurely through it, nevertheless may be regarded as a science from another point of view. Considered as a systematic structure of clearly defined ideal essences giving insight into a "possible world", it must be regarded as meeting the requirements of a science as laid down in chapter three, section A. We saw there that a science is a body of certain and clear abstractive visualizations of intelligible principles of reality systematically interconnected through logical relations. We have here such a visualization of a possible reality. Thus the Aristotelian *a priori* will constitute a science in itself, but it is not a science of the actually existing world. It refers, like the Platonic ideas, though not in the same manner, to another world. A strict correspondence between this science and the actually real natures of things would be purely and simply accidental. With reference to the actual world, this "science" is only a "dialectic", giving a more or less "probable" knowledge.

6. *The philosophy of nature—summary*

But if we consider the philosophy of nature in a wider sense than it has usually been taken, as an investigation not merely

---

1. See *Beta De Caelo*, II, 291b 21-22 ; *Lambda Metaphysicorum*, 8, 1074a 14-17.

2. But Plato's myth seems to be located at the level of perinoetic, rather than dianoetic, knowledge.

of the actual determinations of prime matter but also of its (actually) unrealized potentialities, then this science of ideal essences will pertain to the scientific part of the philosophy of nature. The primary part of the philosophy of nature will then be the generic study of the nature of actually existing mobile being.[1] The secondary part will be the construction of "possible" determinations of matter.[2] This scientific philosophy of nature is then completed by a dialectical viewing of the actually existing mobile being through the medium of these possible structures. (It is precisely with this dialectical viewing in mind that such possible, hypothetical structures are developed dialectically as more or less probable explanations of the detail of phenomena.) Such dialectical procedure is a continuation of the dianoetic tendency of the scientific philosophy of nature, but it is not itself dianoetic in actual termination except in an obscure manner.

Some of our contemporaries seem to regard the knowledge of modern mathematical physics as being a dialectical (in the Aristotelian sense) continuation of the philosophy of nature. Let us now turn to the mode of abstractive visualization in physics, to discover whether its mode of visualization is not altogether distinct from that of the philosophy of nature, and whether it does not constitute a completely autonomous science in itself.

C. ABSTRACTIVE VISUALIZATION IN PHYSICS

1. *Two levels of abstractive visualization in physics*

What kind of abstractive visualization is employed in physics ? It quickly becomes clear that abstractive visualiza-

---

1. It should be noted that we are not speaking of the study of living mobile beings in any way whatsoever. Whether deeper insight into the specific natures of such living things can be gained, we do not seek to know in this discussion. Here the philosophy of nature is viewed only in so far as it studies what is common to both living and non-living mobile being.

2. Whether this philosophy of nature will be *strictly one* science, or a loosely unified group of sciences need not concern us now.

tion is not a univocal term as it is applied to the diverse levels of knowledge within physics. We find a sharp division between the concepts and laws of physics on one hand and its theories on the other. Some have attempted to assimilate physical theory to physical law, regarding a theory as a "synthesis of laws" ; but there still remains a fundamental divergence, which is seen above all at two points.

Firstly, the concept and law directly terminate in the sensible flux ; they are immediate "descriptions" of what is observable "outside" the knower. But the theory is not in immediate relation to objective phenomena ; its immediate termination in the sensible is confined to the imagination, to physical and mathematical "models". Moreover, even this termination in imagination is not essential to a theory. [1] The theory is fundamentally an artificial construct of the intellect, the primary purpose of which is to "unify" and "predict" phenomena—but only through the intermediary of physical concept and law. The theory of itself gives no insight into the real world (not even the real world of phenomena), but only a logical insight into necessary connections which it itself has constituted between concepts and laws through the construction of complex logical entities. [2]

Secondly, the concepts and laws of physics, despite their more intuitive character with respect to the phenomena of the real mobile universe, are viewed in physics as derived "properties" of the theory. The theory is conceived as a center of intelligibility manifesting itself through the phenomena which we describe by our concepts and laws. Thus the theory,

1. R. CARNAP, "Foundations of Logic and Mathematics," *International Encyclopedia of Unified Science*, I, n. 3 (1939), p. 68 : "It is important to realize that the discovery of a model has no more than an aesthetic or didactic or at best a heuristic value, but is not at all essential for a successful application of the physical theory."

2. H. POINCARÉ, *Science and Hypothesis* (New York, 1952), p. 211 : "The object of mathematical theories is not to reveal to us the real nature of things ; that would be an unreasonable claim. Their only object is to co-ordinate the physical laws with which physical experiment makes us acquainted, the enunciation of which, without the aid of mathematics, we should be unable to effect."

although removed from intuitive vision of reality, nevertheless plays in physics a role not unlike that of the philosophical definition in philosophy.[1]

Thus we must affirm the primacy of the concept and law over theory as visualization of the actuality of the mobile real, but the situation is reversed from the standpoint of the logical structure of physics. We shall consider this in greater detail later. For the moment, we merely note the presence in physics of two distinct levels of abstractive visualization. It is necessary to examine each in its turn, in order to ascertain the kind of knowledge of reality conveyed to us through physical science.

2. The definitions of physics

The definitions of physical concepts do not manifest the transphenomenal essence of reality ; they are thus not definitions at all in the traditional sense of the term, since it is precisely the transphenomenal essence which the traditional definition is said to signify. But what is it then that these definitions of physics do signify ?

Since such a definition is not of a transphenomenal essence, it would seem to be of a mere construct, a mere logical entity. But the primary concepts of physics do refer essentially and totally to the sensible manifestations of reality in the sphere of operation. Concepts and definitions are relevant in physics only in so far as they indicate possibilities of observation.[2]

1. E. SIMARD, *La nature et la portée de La Méthode Scientifique* (Quebec, 1956), p. 282 : "Dans les sciences certaines, l'induction conduit à *voir* un principe. En science expérimentale, la théorie qui joue le rôle de principe n'est pas *vue* comme vraie, mais imaginée, ou posée par l'esprit. Au lieu de généraliser une relation découverte dans les singuliers, l'intelligence invente une structure capable du rendre compte des propriétés des gaz ou de l'électricité, par exemple, tout comme la définition du triangle exprime la cause et rend compte de ses propriétés. Pour trouver en physique l'analogue d'une définition philosophique ou mathématique, il semble donc nécessaire de s'en reporter aux théories plutôt qu'à ces groupes de propriétés qu'on appelle communément définitions physiques."

2. A. EINSTEIN, *The Meaning of Relativity*, 5th ed., (Princeton, 1955), p. 2 : "The only justification for our concepts and system of concepts is that

Furthermore, physical concepts must exhibit a quantitative structure. A mere qualitative structure does not possess the precision required for physics. Everything, consequently, must be measured ; the primary content of physical concepts comes to be a group of "pointer readings".[1] The definitions of physics therefore will consist in a series of measurements to be performed, and of calculations to be made.[2]

And yet it is impossible for any physical concept to be purely quantitative. Even measurement presupposes a qualitative diversity between the measuring and the measured.[3]

they serve to represent the complex of our experiences ; beyond this they have no legitimacy. I am convinced that the philosophers have had a harmful effect upon the progress of scientific thinking in removing certain fundamental concepts from the domain of empiricism, where they are under our control, to the intangible heights of the *a priori*. For even if it should appear that the universe of ideas cannot be deduced from experience by logical means, but is, in a sense, a creation of the human mind, without which no science is possible, nevertheless this universe of ideas is just as little independent of the nature of our experience as clothes are of the form of the human body. This is particularly true of our concepts of time and space, which physicists have been obliged by the facts to bring down from the Olympus of the *a priori* in order to adjust them and put them in a serviceable condition."

A. S. EDDINGTON, *Space, Time and Gravitation* (Cambridge, 1923), p. 31 : "... all the familiar terms of physics refer primarily to the relations of the world to an observer in some specified circumstances.

Whether we are able to go still further and obtain a knowledge of the world, which not merely does not particularise the observer, but does not postulate an observer at all ; whether if such knowledge could be obtained, it would convey any intelligible meaning ; and whether it could be of any conceivable interest to anybody if it could be understood—these questions need not detain us now. The answers are not necessarily negative, but they lie outside the normal scope of physics."

1. EDDINGTON, *The Philosophy of Physical Science*, p. 100 : "More generally we must recognize that an item of observational knowledge involves, besides a primary pointer reading, secondary pointer readings identifying the circumstances in which the primary pointer reading occurred. It must be admitted that even an isolated pointer reading is an item of knowledge of a sort ; but it is not with such items that the scientific method deals. For scientific knowledge the association with other pointer readings is an essential condition ; and we may therefore describe physical knowledge as a knowledge of the associations of pointer readings."

2. *Ibid.*, p. 71.

3. F. RENOIRTE, *Cosmology*, trans. J. F. Coffey (New York, 1950), p. 123.

Otherwise, how would we even know their duality ? Even if such measurement were possible, our measurements would all be of the same ; we would not be measuring diverse properties of things. [1] We would not know the difference between types of phenomena to be measured ; we would not draw distinctions between gravitational and electrical phenomena, between magnetic and thermodynamic phenomena.

Clearly then, while the physical concept must exhibit a quantitative structure, this must be seen against a qualitative background. The observable to which physical concepts refer is both qualified and quantified. Physics seeks the quantities here contained, but can only do so by accepting what is, for it, an irrational element, the explanation of which is outside its province—the so-called "secondary qualities". These are assigned to psychology for explanation, but without them there could be no physics.

We should note also that even here in physics it is impossible to avoid some knowledge of being and substance, which lies at the bottom of all our intellectual life. Even in the conception of the "observable", there must be included a vague notion of the transphenomenal "thing". But there is here no clear penetration of its nature—we behold a reality but not in its intrinsic essential intelligibility. We always, even in considering phenomena, abstractly visualize the subject of the change in the world, we never confront a pure flux ; yet here we do not see clearly the transphenomenal nature. Thus even the scientist will speak of "things" (in a transphenomenal sense) in the world, but he will not discuss their ontological nature. As a scientist, he abandons hope of deeper insight into the nature and puts aside that which he has. This is not his concern. Why this renunciation is made in physics we shall consider later.

But, as we have said, the physicist cannot completely renounce the most general and obscure idea of substance. It persists in all his physics in one form or another, as Meyerson

1. *Ibid.*, p. 120.

has so well shown, [1] and as Eddington also has said. [2]   Always he tends toward substance in his efforts to establish conservation laws (laws of permanence even in the midst of change) and to unify phenomenal reality in a stable intelligibility. The physical conception of the permanence of certain quantities in space and time, of ultimate intelligible unities binding the sensible phenomena together, manifests an oblique tendency toward substance.   So it is with the conception of the space-time continuum and of the "nominative of the verb 'to undulate'," which we find lurking in the background of physical undulatory theory.   Yet this tendency toward and blind attainment of substance must never become anything more for physics itself.   For its interest is not in transphenomenal natures as such but in their sensible manifestations.

We might also say that the substance contained in physical concepts is not seen so much as having "sensible matter", but rather mainly as having "intelligible matter", to speak in the technical terminology of St. Thomas Aquinas. [3]   This is to say that we do not see its nature so much as revealed through its qualitative sensible manifestations, but rather mainly as quantified.   Indeed, this substance here is so obscurely seen (since we are not seeking to see it directly) that it may even be confused with pure extension and with the constructed space-time continuum.   It is, perhaps, such confusion of this substance with the constructed logical entities of scientific theory that causes us to hypostatize these entities, thereby committing what Whitehead has called the "fallacy

---

1. *Identity and Reality.*

2. *The Philosophy of Physical Science*, p. 129 : "'Substance' is one of the most dominant concepts in our familiar outlook on the world of sensory experience, and it is one with which science finds itself continually at war. We have already touched on one aspect of it—that it is essentially positive, as contrasted with form which is indifferently positive and negative.   Another attribute of substance is its permanence or semi-permanence ; and in this respect physics has rid itself of the concept of substance only to replace it by something equally permanent.   Indirectly therefore substance still dominates our form of thought—a watered-down substance, of which no attribute survives but its permanence."

3. *Summ. Theol.*, I, q. 85, a. 1, ad 2.

of misplaced concreteness". Here the vague intuition of transphenomenal substance becomes entangled with the logical entities of physics instead of leading us deeper into the transphenomenal being studied by the philosophy of nature.

But to return to the clearly and directly visualized components of the physical concept, we have seen that these are primarily "measurables", quantities in juxtaposition, which are measured by comparison (such is the method of "pointer reading") or by counting. We have seen the necessity also of a qualitative background, a "context" for this quantity. The formal structure of the concept is quantitative, but this structure is seen as embodied in a qualitatively heterogeneous matter.

Thus the physical concept refers to a phenomenal complex (with substance indirectly and obscurely included). The intelligibility of such a concept may be termed intraphenomenal. But such an abstractive visualization falls under what we have earlier called *"perinoetic"* visualization. It is also an *"a posteriori"* visualization, since it visualizes an object beyond the intellect, which was not constructed in and by the intellect, namely, the phenomenal complex in reality itself.

But here we must note that, although this phenomenal complex is not constructed in and by the intellect, nevertheless it may be due in great part to the selective direction of the intellect that the observer or experimenter is presented with *this* phenomenal complex. To obtain a measurable phenomenal complex, and especially, one measurable in the way we wish, it is usually necessary to manufacture physical instruments and to introduce them into the phenomenal structure. Thus the phenomenal complex corresponding to the physical concept is "physically constructed" according to the direction of the intellect (a direction usually conditioned by the already developed structure of physical theory). We may then discern here an *a priori* construction of the concept even before the phenomenal complex imposes the concept on us. For, if the phenomenal complex is to some extent *made* under the direction of the intellect, then it must correspond to an intelligibility already existing in the intellect and constructed by it. Clearly then, the concept of the phenomenal complex has some *a priori* characteristics, and cannot be regarded as a simple *a posteriori* visualization. The only completely *a posteriori* visualization here is of the basic *elements* of the phenomenal complex. Nevertheless, we must insist on this partial and basic *a posteriori* character of the concept of the phenomenal complex ; the complex is in fact a given reality beyond the intellect itself. Hence this kind of concept can truly give intuitive knowledge of the actually (phenomenal) real in its own way, something which an *a priori* conception cannot do precisely in so far as it is *a priori*.

Nevertheless, the fact that the concept of the phenomenal complex has an *a priori* aspect is of great significance for physics. It means that even on this first level of abstractive visualization in physics the world is known in a "selective" manner. Subjectivity enters the "physical" universe already. And yet this subjectivity is not incompatible with the objectivity of physics at this level. It is sometimes argued that, because of the *a priori* direction in selecting the phenomenal complex to be studied, we have destroyed the objective character of physics. This is not at all true. For what has been introduced into the phenomenal complex is not a logical entity but rather other phenomena, even though this has been done under the direction of the intellect with its logical entities. What are being *seen* are still only manifestations of mobile being in the sphere of operation. The subjectivity is a step further back, in the choice of which elements are to be brought together into the phenomenal complex.[1] But clearly, this does not mean that we are seeing through "colored glasses" so as never really to contemplate *natural* phenomena. Rather it would be more proper to say that we merely decide to look in a particular direction rather than in some other direction.

---

1. Even this subjective element is itself traceable to the influence of non-physical, philosophical concepts. This point is discussed in Appendix II.

We are not simply contemplating our own art here ; no, we are using our art to contemplate nature in some, rather than others, of its manifestations. Far from convincing us that nature's manifestations are not being seen in themselves and that we only attain to an intelligibility which we have manufactured, this *a priori* aspect of the concept of the phenomenal complex should remind us that there remains a huge wealth, perhaps, of phenomenal (yet objective) knowledge which we may uncover through the in part *a priori* evolution of new intraphenomenal concepts.

Before giving a concrete example of the physical concept which we have up to now been describing in a rather abstract way, it is necessary to make three further remarks. First, we have spoken of the physical concept as referring to a phenomenal complex. It should be noted that it is usually only one element of the phenomenal complex that directly concerns us. This is some kind of measurable. But the context, as we have indicated, remains absolutely necessary to give meaning to this measurable.

Second, it is quite possible, and indeed usual, that a multitude of different phenomenal contexts will be represented by one unifying concept, in so far as the formal element remains the same, in so far as the measurements in each different context parallel the other measurements in the other contexts, in so far as diverse subsidiary concepts are linked together under one general concept in the framework of the physical theory. For example, the general concept of mass unifies several subsidiary concepts, each of which can be employed with equivalent results if the same body in the same state is placed in the different phenomenal contexts called for by the various subsidiary concepts—there are many ways of determining the same "mass" of a body.

Third, if we take an "operational definition" to be one the elements of which all have intrinsic and immediate reference to the sensible manifestation of mobile being through its operation, then the physical definition and physical concept may be regarded as "operational". We are not using the term "operational" to designate merely a set of operations performed by the scientist,[1] but rather to designate the observed set of physical operations (phenomena) taking place here and now in the mobile universe, regardless of the ultimate source of the operations, whether in the scientist himself or in the environment which he studies. Thus, far from making the meaning of the physical concept to depend solely on the scientist who manipulates things, we make the meaning to depend on an *observable* interaction between things and other things and the observer, in so far as the observer is himself part of this same physical universe. Thus, while man is in the experiment as an agent or transformer, he can also be there as a contemplator of the interaction of the universe of which he himself is a part.

We can now give a concrete illustration of what is meant by a physical concept. But we shall consider only an already-developed concept. We shall not attempt to trace the formation of a new physical concept ; this would require an account of the philosophical ideas and theoretical structure which influence and direct this development, an account that would take us far beyond what is here necessary.

Consider the meaning of the proposition, "This piece of gold has a mass of two grams". We have here the physical concept of *mass*. Newton regarded mass as the "quantity of matter",[2] which would seem to be an ontological conception. But today, physics conceives mass only with reference to observable characteristics of bodies. Mass is a number obtained through setting the body in a certain operational context. Fundamentally, this number is obtained by a comparison, ultimately with a *standard of mass*. There must be a set of operations, such as the use of a balance under proper conditions, which will result in a pointer-reading on a scale. This same set of operations could be performed on the standard of mass as well. But the standard must be determined through

1. This, however, seems to be the meaning given to it by P. W. BRIDGMAN, *The Logic of Modern Physics* (New York, 1927), p. 5.

2. Isaac NEWTON, *Mathematical Principles*, Definition I.

some other criterion, to avoid an elementary vicious circle. It may be through the measurement of a definite volume of a definite material at a definite temperature and pressure—not that we ever escape a radical relativity in all physical measurement.

But this set of operations and of phenomena, which yield the measurement called mass, are themselves also to be measured. The balance must be characterized by definite quantitatively measurable properties, such as the rigidity of its parts, the equal length of each arm, etc. Thus, mass is not given simply by one pointer-reading in a qualitative context, but by this pointer-reading accompanied by a whole series of other pointer-readings in a qualitative context. Theoretically, this process of obtaining pointer-readings could be carried to infinity, if we were to measure the instruments of measurement of measurement, etc. In practice, we content ourselves with a comparatively small number, which serve to indicate adequately the applicability of the concept, on the assumption that the phenomenal universe has some order and uniformity, and that much of it is not too great a disturbing factor in the measurement at hand. This introduces an element of approximation into our measurements, which cannot be avoided. We would have to have an intuitive knowledge of all the quantitative states of the entire universe simultaneously in order to obtain an exact measurement. An attempt to get an exact measurement will inevitably lead us into conflict with anyone else who is trying to get an exact measurement, since each must measure everything in the universe. Indeed, even the separate measurements of the same measurer, or of his assistants, would interfere with each other. As Mr. Eddington tells us, "One perfect observer is a nuisance. Two perfect observers make a fight. Three perfect observers send us fleeing for refuge to the concept of probability."[1]

Of course, the set of operations required to obtain the mass may be other than the use of a balance. One might employ

1. *The Philosophy of Physical Science*, p. 98.

a mass-spectrograph for small quantities, or one might measure the gravitational attraction between two bodies, or one might measure the velocity produced by given "forces" in a given time, etc. Each of these will require a whole series of measured quantities just as the first method did. But furthermore, each of these methods can only be used on condition that one accept a whole body of theoretical knowledge. Indeed, even the first method requires the acceptance of a body of theoretical knowledge. We must assume in the first method (the use of the balance) the approximate validity of Newtonian mechanics, in the second method the theory of electromagnetism and the atomic theory of matter, in the third method Newtonian and even Einsteinian (if the measurements are on a large scale or are very precise) mechanics, in the fourth method Newtonian mechanics again. We must assume for all of these measurements a definite theory of optics and of thermodynamics, etc., etc. In short, the physical determination of mass can only be made in a theoretical context of great complexity.

Thus the concept of mass carries in itself the mark of subjectivity as well as of objectivity. It is manufactured by us to mould reality as well as at the same time to know reality. It is at once both practical and speculative. It is *a priori* as well as *a posteriori*, *a priori* in so far as it guides the selection of phenomena, *a posteriori* in so far as its elements correspond to phenomena which are really there to be known, and which really impose themselves on our knowing powers.

We may now note again that the concept of mass is actually a plurality of concepts, corresponding to the diverse modes of determining the mass. These concepts are all linked together under one general concept in and through the physical theory.

Is there, however, a primary concept of mass, imposed on us by the real? It seems that the concept of mass may originate in the feeling of resistance to motion, but it is equally clear that this is not the concept of mass employed in physics. We may say that common experience provides us with a "scaffolding" for the construction of the physical concept of mass, but this scaffolding falls away when the developed concept is achieved in physics itself.   Historically, the concept of mass was not purified of ontological resonances in the physics of Newton, as we have said above ; but this is no longer true in contemporary physics.   The physical concept must now contain nothing that does not designate a "possibility of observation".

What we have said of mass may also be said of the other element of our proposition, "This piece of gold has a mass of two grams".   What do we mean by gold ?   Gold will be defined in physics and chemistry in terms of its observable, measurable properties.   For example, gold will be considered as an element of atomic weight 197.2, of atomic number 79, of valence positive one or three, of electrode potential negative 1.68, etc.

However, these concepts do carry an obscure reference to substance.   Mass is not conceived as an aspect of a pure flux ; it is an attribute of a "thing".   Similarly, gold is here the name of a "thing" which manifests itself in definite ways under definite conditions.

It is similar in the case of other concepts and definitions of physics.   All will be found to have direct reference only to possibilities for observation, to the extent that they are truly physical.[1]   To the extent that they do not have such reference, they are rightly dismissed by the scientist as "metaphysical".   His observation is not of the *being* of things, except in an oblique way, but rather of the sensible manifestations of being in the sphere of operation.

To summarize then concerning the concept in physics.   It is *a posteriori*, when considered with respect to the components of the phenomenal complex.   But it is partially *a priori*, when considered with respect to the *selection* and *structure* of these

---

1. But substance, obscurely known, is contained in the physical concept, as we have already said, since phenomena cannot be known without at least indirect reference to substantial being.   In the knowledge of accidents must be included a knowledge of substance.

components. The *elements* are imposed on us ; the *pattern* is our own work, though not completely. Finally, the physical concept does not refer directly to the transphenomenal *nature* of reality, but rather to its sensible *manifestations ;* this makes it properly *perinoetic* knowledge.

The content and scope of physical concepts must be specified precisely. This means that these concepts must provide us with distinct actual and distinct virtual knowledge of the phenomena. Such knowledge is requisite for any science, as we said in chapter three ; but more is also required. This knowledge must be bound up into a stable *unity* through logical relations, if we are to have true science. It is impossible to accomplish this unification in physics on the level of the phenomenal concept itself. It is necessary to rise to the higher level of theory through the intermediary of law. We shall now see how this is done.

3. *The laws of physics*

The concepts of physics are integrated into a higher unity by the physical law. The law again is an abstractive visualization of the phenomena, but it is this only in virtue of its immediate function of relating physical concepts to each other. We have already indicated above that the content of the physical concept is formally quantitative and only materially qualitative. It is the quantity formally given in the physical concept which can be related to other quantities given in other such concepts. Physical law states functional relationships between variable quantities of this kind (it may also state the constancy of certain quantities, under definite quantitative conditions ; e. g., the conservation of mass in classical physics, which itself pertains properly to the theoretical level of physics, implies phenomenal laws of this kind).

Because the physical law cannot penetrate reality in any deeper way than the physical concepts which are its elements, the physical law also contains only an *intraphenomenal* intelligibility. Thus the physical law remains *perinoetic* in character.

But we speak of some physical laws as being discovered in experiment and of others as being deduced from theory. Does this mean that some are *a priori* while others are *a posteriori?* Unfortunately it is not quite so simple. Every law has an *a priori* aspect, in so far as the concepts which it contains have themselves an *a priori* aspect. But every law has an *a posteriori* aspect as well, in so far as the concepts which it contains have in themselves an *a posteriori* aspect. Nevertheless, the *a priori* character of some laws is more marked than that of others. So-called "empirical" laws participate in the *a priori* only to the extent that their constitutive concepts do. Of this kind would be the law of spectral line frequencies of hydrogen, before it received a theoretical interpretation from Bohr. Clearly, those laws resulting from new deduction from theories are most *a priori* with respect to their formation, although, to the extent that they are confirmed by observation, they also become *a posteriori*. Of this kind is the law of the displacement of spectral lines under a gravitational field, as given by Einstein's general theory of relativity.

Since the physical law is essentially an expression of mathematical functionality (whether deterministic or statistical), of the relationship between quantitative variables and constants, the law will receive its most appropriate expression in an algebraic formula. The phenomenal laws consequent upon the Newtonian "laws" of motion can be expressed in verbal formulae, but it is their quantitative form which is of most interest to physics.

Although quantitative by its essence, the physical law refers in an oblique way to the qualitative as well, since the constitutive concepts are materially qualitative. The laws do not have significance for physics without reference to this qualitative real. But because the form of these laws is itself purely quantitative, it is possible to reason with them in a purely mathematical way. It is possible—at least it is the attempt of physics—to exhibit them as logical and mathematical consequences of constructed theories. Through such

theories, a multitude of laws may be bound into a higher
logical unity. With this, we shall attain to the unified yet
complex abstractive visualization that we call science. But
we shall find that the theory stands on an entirely different
level of intellection from that of the concept and law.

4. *The theories of physics*

Physical science achieves its highest unity in and through
the physical theory.[1] But it is necessary to distinguish
between the physical theory *in the strict sense* and the physical
theory *in the wide sense*. We shall begin with a discussion
of the former.

In what does a physical theory consist ? It is sometimes
described as a mathematical structure[2] and sometimes as a
logical structure.[3] We shall consider this point later—for
the moment we may be content to say that the theory is a
structure of *symbols*, to be interpreted one way or the other.
It is from the given laws expressed in a symbolic form that
we are led to make the theoretical structure, which can be
regarded, in some respects, as a "synthesis of laws". The
laws in their symbolic form must be deducible from the theory.
But the theory is not deducible from the laws ; it remains a
hypothetical construction.[4] A sign of this is the fact that
several theories may be constructed to account for the same
facts ; indeed it may be extremely difficult, if not impossible,
even to devise tests for preferring one theory over another.[5]

But the theory nevertheless holds in science a place analogous to that which the knowledge of a real nature holds in

1. A. EINSTEIN, *Relativity*, trans. R. W. Lawson, 15th ed. (London, 1955),
pp. 123-124.

2. P. DUHEM, *The Aim and Structure of Physical Theory*, trans. P. Wiener
(Princeton, 1954), p. 19.

3. *Ibid.*, p. 31.

4. A. EINSTEIN, "The Fundaments of Theoretical Physics," *Readings
in the Philosophy of Science*, ed. H. Feigl and M. Brodbeck (New York, 1953),
p. 253.

5. EINSTEIN, *Relativity*, p. 124.

philosophy. The philosophical nature naturally manifests itself in the phenomena and is the real principle of their intelligibility ; the physical theory logically "manifests" itself in the physical laws of the phenomena and becomes the principle (artificial and logical) of their intelligibility.[1] The theory thus gives to physics its fully scientific character as a unified and stable set of abstractive visualizations of the intelligible principles of phenomenal reality in its phenomenality.

But these intelligible principles of phenomena in their phenomenality pertain entirely to the sphere of formal causality, since the material cause does not of itself appear to us but only through its forms, and since efficient and final causality are operative, not precisely in the sphere of the phenomena themselves but in the sphere of the existent which produces the phenomena. Thus, the theory fulfills its function if and only if it gives us a unified grasp of the formal causes of phenomena.

But how can it accomplish this if it is merely a structure of logical or mathematical symbols ? It is altogether necessary that at least some of the symbols (those which will appear in the deduced laws as variables) be given a meaning in observational terms.[2] In other words, they must correspond to what we have above called physical concepts. Thus the theory must include a set of "operational definitions" (in the sense which we have given to this term earlier) as a dictionary for the symbols. These provide rules of translation from the symbolic theoretical structure to the understanding of qualitative and quantitative phenomena.

The theory, as a structure of logical or mathematical sym-

---

1. MARITAIN, *Les Degrés du Savoir*, p. 111.

2. EDDINGTON, *The Philosophy of Physical Science*, p. 33 : "It is never the task of the experimenter to devise the observational procedure which is the *ultimate* test of a scientific assertion. That must be indicated unambiguously in the assertion itself, having regard to the definitions of the terms employed in it ; otherwise it is incapable of submission to the Court of Appeal, and is inadmissible as an item of physical knowledge. Where the ingenuity of the experimenter is often required is in devising a procedure equivalent to, but more practicable than, the procedure referred to in the assertion."

bols, clearly has no real existence independently of the mind. But it is constructed on the basis of the relations between phenomena as grouped in physical concepts and laws. Hence, the structure is to be regarded, in scholastic terminology, as a logical entity founded in reality (an *ens rationis cum fundamento in re*). But, this foundation is not directly in the transphenomenal natures of things, but only in their phenomena. We do not have here any basis for affirming some dim insight into the essence of reality, or anything of the kind. [1]

Before attempting to outline the epistemological characteristics of a physical theory in the strict sense, we must say a few more words about the nature of its symbolic structure. We said that it has been diversely characterized as mathematical and logical. This seems to demand some explanation.

First, the laws of phenomena which physics must unify are themselves quantitative (mathematical) in nature. It would seem then that the unifying theories would themselves necessarily be mathematical in character. But unfortunately the case is not quite so simple.

What is mathematics ? Until the last century, mathematics was regarded as the science of *quantity*. In the Thomist tradition, mathematics studies quantity, which, although not found in a "purified" state in *physical reality*, is nevertheless clearly presented to us apart from sensible qualities through *imaginative intuition*. [2] The object of mathematics as such is not found immediately in the sensible but it is disengaged in the imaginable.

But with the development of non-Euclidean geometries, which do not themselves refer to the primary quantitative objects known through imaginative intuition, it seemed necessary to admit that the traditional concept of mathematics must be inadequate. This seemed even more so with the

---

1. For a position apparently claiming such a physical knowledge of the nature of things, see MEYERSON, *Identity and Reality*, p. 395.

As we shall show later, there is a certain truth here ; but we must say that the theory *as such* has a purely phenomenal reference.

2. ST. THOMAS AQUINAS, *In De Trinitate*, q. 6, a. 1 ; MARITAIN, *Les Degrés du Savoir*, pp. 280-282.

evolution of "mathematical" structures which seemed to be not even of a directly quantitative character. Mathematics appeared to be becoming a study of pure relations, not a study of quantitative relations.

But such a study of pure relations, without determinate content, is also the concern of modern mathematical logic. The evolution of mathematics and logic led inevitably to the confusion of mathematics and logic. Thus it is that the same structure is characterized as both mathematical and logical. Indeed, it is even maintained that logic and mathematics are not distinguishable. And such is in fact the case, if we consider each as the study of pure relations. [1]

While admitting the possibility of such a study of relations (and calling it formal logic), it is still possible to study quantity (and this study I will call mathematics—but see Appendix I), either directly or analogically attained. Always acknowledging a certain priority for what can be constructed in reference to imaginative intuition, we may also regard other constructions (such as in group theory or non-Euclidean geometry) as properly mathematical in so far as they are considered as analogous to the directly imaginable. These same analogically quantitative (whether remaining formally quantitative, as in the case of the various non-Euclidean geometries and the investigations of topology, or passing over from properly quantitative reality to that of metaphysical multiplicity, as in the case of group theory) constructions, when cut off from all reference to imaginative intuition, or indeed to any intuition of some mode of real being, may come to belong to the sphere of formal logic alone, in so far as we now have a system of relations without determinate content. Mathematics should resist this transformation into formal logic, [2]

1. But, in addition to the remarks which immediately follow, see Appendix I on the meanings of "mathematics".

2. One may also point out, however, that this "logic" is not the whole of logic in the traditional Thomistic sense. For St. Thomas, logic studies the order obtaining between the intentions of the intellect *(ordo quam intellectus adinvenit in suas intentiones)*; similarly, for Maritain, logic finds its proper object in the objects of the other sciences in so far as they are considered

or at least it should be conscious of the transformation.[1]

The symbolic structures of physical theory may be considered as mathematical throughout, so long as we admit the possibility of "analogically quantitative" objects for mathematics—as, for example, in geometry, where the directly imaginable three-dimensional "space-like" manifold may help us to an analogical understanding of "space-like" manifolds of more than three dimensions. Or these symbolic structures of physical theory may also be considered as purely logical—a network of relational forms without determinate content, which receive a mathematical (and then a physical) interpretation when deductions from this structure reach the level of what is regarded as phenomenal law.

It seems then that the physical theory may, *precisely in its character as a symbolic structure*, indifferently be regarded as having a determinate (mathematical) content or not. But even if it is regarded as having a mathematical content, this structure does not directly and in itself represent the real natures of things any more than does any other mathematical construction. With such a content, the theory becomes a "mathematical model" ; but this is not the nature of reality.

Before seeing an example of a physical theory, let us summarize its characteristics as a knowledge of nature. Because the construction of a theory is a work of the mind, because the theory is not *necessitated* and imposed on us by the phenomena, it is clear that physical theory is *a priori* knowledge. Since the theoretical structure, apart from the "dictionary" of operational definitions which translate its ultimate deductions into phenomenal laws, gives no intuitive grasp of the phenomena themselves, it must be regarded as completely *a priori*.[2]

in the mind (*Les Degrés du Savoir*, pp. 282-283). This modern "logic", however, would study pure forms, pure relations, independently of any determinate contents and elements. This logic corresponds to traditional *formal* logic, though it attains a greater abstractness than the traditional logic.

1. The ideas of this paragraph are suggested by Jacques Maritain's *Les Degrés du Savoir*, pp. 279-284. For further amplification, see Appendix I.

2. This, however, does not deny an ultimate reference to the sensible phenomena, with respect to the *first elements of construction*.

And yet the theoretical structure has an intrinsic and essential, though mediate, reference to the real observable, as we have said above. Because it thus contributes to our understanding of the *phenomena* rather than of the transphenomenal natures, we can call it *perinoetic* knowledge.

But the perinoetic knowledge of the physical theory (even considered as a mathematical structure) differs from the perinoetic knowledge of the physical concept and law ; for, as we have just said, it is non-intuitive in relation to the phenomena, even while retaining an intrinsic reference to these phenomena. It is now helpful to distinguish two levels of perinoetic knowledge. Knowledge which refers immediately to the phenomena themselves we may call *first level* perinoetic knowledge. Knowledge which refers to the phenomena intrinsically but only mediately we may term *second level* perinoetic knowledge. Thus the physical concept and physical law, even though they contain some *a priori* structure, are *first level* perinoetic knowledge ; but the physical theory is *second level* perinoetic knowledge.

As an example of such a symbolic theoretical structure, which yields deductively the actual laws of phenomena, we may consider Newtonian mechanics as interpreted by a contemporary physicist. [1] Newtonian mechanics has been surpassed by relativity and quantum mechanics, but this does not detract from its theoretical value in predicting a wide range of phenomena with a high degree of accuracy. [2] But "Newtonian" mechanics is not the same thing as the mechanics of Newton. Despite the attribution of positivism to Newton, [3] there is much reason to doubt that Newton himself was a thorough positivist in his physics. His concepts and theories appear at times to have more than a merely perinoetic aim. [4]

---

1. See, for example, K. R. Symon, *Mechanics* (Cambridge, 1953).
2. *Ibid.*, p. 9.
3. Brewster, *Memoirs of the Life, Writings, and Discoveries of Sir Isaac Newton* (Edinburgh, 1855), II, 532 (cited in E. A. Burtt, *The Metaphysical Foundations of Modern Science*, Garden City, N. Y., 1955, p. 227).
4. See, for example, *Mathematical Principles*, Definitions, Scholium.

Here we are considering Newtonian mechanics as purified of such "ontological" concerns.

At the heart of Newtonian mechanics there are four definitions, a mathematical technique, and four so-called "laws". The definitions are those of position, time, force and mass. The technique is that of the calculus, a mathematical device for handling functional relationships between variable quantities (here primarily force, mass, time, and position). The "laws" are Newton's laws of motion and law of gravitation. The basic problem of this classical mechanics is to determine functions which specify the positions of objects as functions of time. [1] The meaning of "position at a certain time" is operational, that is, it "is contained in the rules which tell us how to measure the coordinate x of a particle at a time t." [2] The operational character of the definition of mass has already been explained above. Force is *defined*, by Symon, as the quantity *ma* (mass times the rate of change of the rate of change of position).

With such operational definitions forming the elements of a dictionary for the symbolic structure, we may now consider the *axioms* of this structure. These are the laws of motion and the law of gravitation. [3] It must first be noted that these are not laws in the ordinary sense of physical law as a description of the regularity of phenomena. We cannot *observe* that Newton's laws hold. For they are not a simple description of our experience ; they represent an idealization, an abstraction, and an interpretation. As Poincaré has pointed out, they are conventions ; [4] this is to say that they exist on the level of physical theory rather than of physical law. They represent a constructed *a priori*.

With these fundamental axioms, together with the accompanying mathematical rules of manipulation and the operational interpretations of the symbols, [5] it is already possible to

1. SYMON, *op. cit.*, p. 4.
2. *Ibid.*
3. *Ibid.*, pp. 7-10.
4. POINCARÉ, *Science and Hypothesis*, pp. 135-136.
5. We do not here discuss the *choice of units* in which to express the measured quantities. This belongs to the sphere of the operational definitions.

unify and to predict many phenomena of a relatively simple order. [1]

For a more complete unification of phenomena, it is necessary to develop, by mathematical construction and deduction, more complex "second level axioms", or theorems, such as those concerning the rate of change of momentum and of kinetic energy, and more complex concepts such as this momentum and kinetic energy. [2] Note that these theorems are not observational laws ; they do not immediately refer to observable phenomena. In themselves they are only a part of the symbolic structure ; only at the point where theorems can be interpreted immediately through operational definitions are such theorems translated into "physical laws," in our sense of the term. The symbolic structure becomes more complex and the rules of manipulation become more varied. We see the concept of potential energy appear, [3] and the law of conservation of energy follow. [4] We see new mathematical techniques introduced—those of vector algebra. [5] So the construction of theoretical mechanics proceeds, to ever greater complexity—and yet also to greater unity.

Because physical theory becomes physical law precisely at the point where the operational definitions of the symbols are added to give a phenomenal interpretation, the law has an ambivalent character. Its symbolic expression may be assimilated to the theoretical symbolic structure, while its phenomenal interpretations may not be so assimilated. Here is the point of contact between symbol and reality, albeit only phenomenal reality.

But in Newtonian mechanics, we may point out, the ideal of *unification* was very imperfectly achieved. The mechanical and gravitational laws remained simply diverse ; the equality of gravitational and inertial mass remained a mere unex-

1. SYMON, *op. cit.*, pp. 12-17.
2. *Ibid.*, pp. 20-21.
3. *Ibid.*, p. 29.
4. *Ibid.*
5. *Ibid.*, pp. 61-78.

plained *fact*. It remained for Einstein to simplify greatly the entire body of theoretical mechanics by his general theory of relativity ; but this development need not concern us here.

Despite the fact that these theories "in the strict sense" are merely symbolic structures with at best a purely mathematical significance, we can sometimes see a tendency toward "realistic substantialism" in their interpretation. For the mathematical structures are at times regarded as somehow in correspondence with the stable natures of concrete reality. This is the mistake which Whitehead has labeled the "fallacy of misplaced concreteness".[1] This mistake was much more characteristic of the science of the sixteenth through the nineteenth centuries, but we find it even in the twentieth century in scientists like Sir James Jeans,[2] despite the sharp criticisms of positivistic logicians.

Why has this fallacy existed in the past and even persisted until now ? It seems that there are two fundamental reasons for confusing this mathematical essence with the real substantial natures of reality. The first of these would appear to be entirely plausible. Clearly, the real nature is the real principle of the operations which we observe. Especially if there are a number of such operations, the constructed mathematical essence which itself also, though in a line of "logical causality", principiates these operations (in their quantitative aspects) would seem necessarily to bear *some* similarity to the substantial essence. We have here an *analogy* between two essences, the natural and the artificial (mathematical), in that they both have intrinsic reference to the same set of operations.

The second reason is not so much "reasonable", as "psychological". It rests in a confusion which arises because of the mode and conditions of conceptualization of the mathematical structures in physics. Although such structures are logical entities *(entia rationis)*, they are always *conceived* after the manner of *being*, after the manner of *substantial being*. And

1. A. N. WHITEHEAD, *Science and the Modern World* (New York, 1956). p. 52.

2. Sir James JEANS, *The Mysterious Universe* (New York, 1930), p. 158.

these structures are always conceived with intrinsic reference to physical concepts and physical laws. But, at these lower levels of concept and law, a notion of substance is obscurely contained in every item of knowledge, as we have seen above. This notion of substance may easily pass out of its proper place into this higher theoretical level of science. There takes place here a simple confusion regarding the location by the intellect of what was only grasped most obscurely in the first place—material substance. Such "misplaced concreteness" can easily occur where the philosophical significance of real substance and of logical entities has not been clearly seen.

This second reason need not be subjected to deeper critical analysis here—its foundation in a lack of clear philosophical apprehension of reality is sufficiently evident. We are here confronted not so much with a flaw in philosophical or scientific *reasoning* as with an "optical illusion of the intellect", which "sees" in a distorted manner because it has failed to develop adequately its philosophical insight.

Concerning the first reason, however, it is necessary to make several remarks. First, the real specific nature can only be manifested through qualitative differences in its operations. Quantity is not a principle of differentiation but only of divisibility. Therefore, the quantitative structures of scientific theory do not, in themselves, reveal specific natures. Second, if these structures predict the phenomena, they do so *as a whole*. The whole structure predicts the totality of (quantitative) phenomena.[1] Therefore, it is not possible to set up rigid correspondences between discrete parts of this structure and discrete parts of the phenomenal real, which would be necessary if we were to learn something of the substantial natures through these structures. Finally, as we have already seen and will see still further, the mode of insight in physical science is entirely different from that in the philosophical study of substantial natures. The interest of the intellect is

---

1. DUHEM, *The Aim and Structure of Physical Theory*, pp. 199-200.

entirely turned away from substantial natures in physics and towards the phenomena. It views these phenomena through the medium of mathematical structure, itself the product of a non-ontological science.

And yet, despite this radically different orientation of physics, it would still seem that, from a wider viewpoint, the structures of physics do after all have an intimate connection with the substantial natures. For predictions made on the basis of these structures *are* verified in the operations of the things themselves, operations which are at the same time controlled by the substantial natures. Even though this theoretical structure is not the nature, and does not formally represent the nature as it really is, still it must be said to be *symbolic* of the nature. But it would be altogether beyond the scope of physics itself to consider this symbolism philosophically in its relation to the symbolized real nature. This is in the province of metaphysics. The method of physics stops short at the construction of theory and the prediction of phenomena on the basis of such theory.

Concerning prediction, another remark must be made. It is not enough that a physical theory correlate the phenomena up to now discovered. It should also stimulate further research. This stimulus is often achieved through the mental transposition of the ideal structure of the theory into the real order of things or into some new domain of the real order of things. Here it may be seen to possess entirely new properties, properties which it does not need in order to account for the phenomena already known, properties which logically necessitate other phenomena not yet known. This is the prediction of new phenomena ; if such phenomena are actually discovered, the theory is said to be confirmed. From this point of view, the tendency toward "realistic substantialism" within physics can result in great advances in physics, even though it would lead to philosophical error when elevated to the status of a philosophical principle. We could regard this tendency to realistic substantialism as a *methodological principle* in physics, which does not reflect any philosophical opinion concerning the nature of things at all. Unfortunately, this methodological principle of physics has been elevated by some into a manner of attaining (or rather of hoping to attain) the truth about the nature of things, as we have pointed out above.

The substantialized logical entities of physics have been termed by L. W. Beck "inferred entities".[1] An "inferred entity" for him "is the supposed real existent whose existence is inferred if and only if a given substantive hypothetical proposition about it is confirmed. Or : an inferred entity is the supposedly real existent corresponding to the antecedent of a substantive hypothetical proposition."[2] Mr. Beck shows the value of such "inferred entities" in physics as an aid in the prediction of new phenomena ; indeed, he maintains that such substantialization, ruled out by positivism, is a highly desirable step in the advancement of physics, and gives an excellent example in the discovery of Graham's law of diffusion.[3]

But by now the reader may have noted that in this "substantialization" of the formal structures of physics, of the theory in the narrow sense, besides the always necessary operational interpretations at the level where theory becomes law, an interpretation in imagination of at least the higher levels of the formal structure itself becomes necessary. For, if we are to think this structure as really existing,[4] we must do so by endowing it with at least some of the (observable) attributes of other existents. In other words, we must construct a *physical model*, in which to embody the theory. It is the addition of this physical model which gives us physical theory "in the wide sense".

The structural portion of the theory still remains central in the science ; the physical model is only an auxiliary. The

---

1. L. W. BECK, "Constructions and Inferred Entities", *Philosophy of Science*, 17 (1950), reprinted in H. Feigl and M. Brodbeck, *Readings in the Philosophy of Science*, pp. 368-381.

2. *Ibid.*, pp. 369-370.

3. *Ibid.*, pp. 380-381.

4. But we must note that "existence", in physics, is synonymous with "being observable".

proper function of this model is to enable us to achieve a better grasp of the abstract formal structure and to help us to see new lines along which this structure may be developed in order to predict new phenomena. Thus the function of this model is both didactic and heuristic.

But if the *physical model* is a work of the imagination, it is essentially "observable to the imagination" and it is constructed from what is itself observable to sense or to imagination. "Observable to imagination" includes even the purely quantitative constructions which are called mechanical models. Indeed, it may include not only the direct appearance of quantitative structures in imaginative intuition, but even the basis in imaginative intuition for the analogically quantitative structures such as non-Euclidean geometrical models, or for certain abstract logical structures.

Since the theoretical structure itself refers immediately (directly or analogically) to the imaginative model (constructed to embody the theory) we have a special kind of perinoetic knowledge of the *first level* given by this theoretical structure in reference to this imaginative model. Thus the theoretical structure is both first and second level perinoetic knowledge, but from different points of view. The second level perinoetic knowledge here is of the essence of the theory in the strict sense, while the first level perinoetic knowledge is a *per accidens* characteristic of such a theory, due only to the construction of the physical model in the imagination. This first level perinoetic knowledge through the theory therefore in no way refers to the real world (but only to the imagined world of physical models), while the second level perinoetic knowledge of the theory has essential, though mediate, reference to the real phenomenal world.

The use of physical models presents dangers to physical science from two points of view. The construction of a physical model to embody a theoretical formal structure tends to heighten the illusion we have already spoken of, that this formal structure is the nature of reality itself. When the physical model is added, we are no longer contemplating a mere abstract mathematical or logical structure, but a concrete "cosmic image". From a critical philosophical viewpoint, this is not the ultimate real nature of things ; but if the formal structure taken in itself can be mistakenly regarded as representing the transphenomenal nature of reality, how much greater the temptation so to regard this formal structure now that it is concretely embodied in the physical model ?

The second danger is that such a physical model may itself be regarded as constituting a *philosophical interpretation* of the theoretical formal structure, a "myth" about the nature of things developed on the basis of physical theory. But we have seen that this model is itself constructed in the *imagination*. It does not in itself represent to us even a hypothetical nature. And the interest of physics in this model is entirely perinoetic. The physical model, just as any image before the abstracting and constructing intellect, may suggest to the philosopher some ideal constructions, with which he will create the "philosophical myth" that we have spoken of above in the section on the philosophy of nature. But the physical model is not itself such a philosophical myth for the simple reason that it is not in itself intellectual but only imaginative.

5. *Summary of abstractive visualization in physics*

To summarize briefly our account of abstractive visualization in physics, we may say that it is everywhere *perinoetic*. No attempt is made to know the *nature* of reality through physical concepts in themselves ; this is prohibited by the very requirements for a physical concept. The nature is transphenomenal, while the physical concept must refer wholly to measurable phenomena. The theoretical structure of physics is a construction of the mind the aim of which is simply to link these concepts and measurables to other such concepts and measurables. Everywhere it must have intrinsic, though mediate, reference to the measurable phenomena. Since the theoretical construction is logical or mathematical in nature and since it is made by the mind solely on the basis of and in reference to the measurable phenomena, it cannot itself be representative of the nature of reality. Although such theoretical constructions must be regarded as symbolic of the nature of reality, it is not within the province of physics to speculate about the relationship of such symbols to the symbolized transphenomenal natures. This is a problem for metaphysics and the philosophy of nature.

Within the body of physical knowledge we may distinguish two main levels of abstractive visualization, one which is intuitive with respect to the real phenomena and another which is not. The first is subdivided into the levels of concept and law. Both of these give *a posteriori* knowledge with respect to the elements of the phenomenal complex, but each includes a constructed *a priori* pattern in the visualized phenomenal complex. In so far as these two levels of perinoetic knowledge terminate directly in real phenomena, they can be called *first level* perinoetic knowledge.

The second main level of abstractive visualization in physical science is that of physical theory. Here the formal structure which is the theory proper is in no way an *a posteriori* visualization ;[1] rather it is a completely *a priori* construction, not imposed on us by the phenomena. Since it does not terminate immediately in real phenomena, it can be called *second level* perinoetic knowledge. However, when this formal structure is considered in relation to the imagined phenomena comprising the physical model, the formal structure becomes *per accidens* a first level perinoetic knowledge.

This latter form of first level perinoetic knowledge may result not only from theoretical constructions which refer

---

1. Of course, the elements of any construction are ultimately derived a posteriori from an intuitive grasp of reality in some way. But this ultimate origin of such elements is not sufficient to constitute them as a posteriori knowledge, precisely as they are employed in the constitution of the theoretical structure of physics.

directly to imagined phenomena but also from those which refer only analogically to imagined phenomena, in so far as the analogically quantitative constructions of higher mathematics or certain constructions of abstract logic have been used in such theoretical constructions of physics.

CHAPTER V

THE OBJECT IN THE PHILOSOPHY OF NATURE AND IN PHYSICAL SCIENCE

A. THE PROBLEM

In the previous chapter, we described some characteristics of abstractive visualization in the philosophy of nature and in physical science. This was primarily a discussion of some *methods* of knowing reality in these sciences. It is necessary now, in the light of this preceding discussion, to consider whether or not two completely distinct *objects* are attained in these sciences. According to the criterion that we laid down in chapter one, the differentiation of sciences from each other is in accordance with the differentiation of their objects. In view of what we have said up to now, is it possible to distinguish completely physics and the philosophy of nature according to this criterion ?

Let us recall briefly several points from chapter one. It was necessary to distinguish two objects of intellectual knowledge, the material object and the formal object. The material object is the thing itself in its complete and inexhaustible (for us) intelligibility. The formal object is that "part" or perfection of the thing which momentarily terminates the outgoing movement of the intellect in contemplation, and through which some wider portion of the total intelligibility may perhaps be seen (but only through the long continued and repeated ever deepening gaze of the intellect, and, if possible, with the help of "scientific demonstration"). The distinction of sciences is according to the distinction of *formal* object.

Formal objects of speculative intellectual knowledge are distinct from each other according as one is more immaterial than another. This does not mean merely that one is more separated from matter (the *terminus a quo* of intellectual abstraction) than another. Rather, it primarily means that one object is constituted by a higher degree of actuality (the *terminus ad quem* of intellectual abstraction) than another. For scientific knowing does not consist merely in separation of an object from matter ; it is primarily a visualization of *actuality*.

But this "formal object" was seen to be twofold. Since the formal object is an aspect of the thing both in its real existence and in its existence as known, we distinguish between the formal object *in the thing (ratio formalis obiecti ut res)* and the formal object *in the intellect (ratio formalis obiecti ut obiectum)*. It is according to this latter that the distinction of sciences is first determined, and it is according to the former that this distinction of sciences receives its explanation.

When the formal object *in the thing* cannot be adequately conceived in one given way, it is possible that there is more than one formal object *in the intellect* (and therefore more than one science) corresponding to the one formal object *in the thing*. But if this happens, the formal object in the thing must be radically divisible (intrinsically or extrinsically) in some way. For a purely subjective diversity of formal objects in the intellect (and therefore of sciences) would lead to a vicious circle in which the diversity of abstracting sciences would be due to the diversity of formal objects abstracted, while the diversity of formal objects abstracted would be due to the diversity of the abstracting sciences.

The formal object in the thing is called by Maritain an intelligibility-appeal of first determination. Its radical divisibility, which grounds the diversity of formal objects in the intellect, makes us distinguish in this intelligibility-appeal of first determination some intelligibility-appeals of second determination.

If two sciences of the real, then, are to be adequately and intelligibly diversified according to their formal objects, it is not sufficient to distinguish merely the methods of abstractive visualization or the formal objects in the intellect alone. It is further necessary to ground this distinction of objects in the intellect in some distinction of formal object in the reality itself, at least in some radical divisibility (intrinsic or extrinsic) in this formal object in reality. If, corresponding to the same intelligibility-appeal of first determination, we find diverse modes of abstractive visualization and a diversity of formal objects in the intellect, it is still necessary to show how there are correspondingly diverse intelligibility-appeals of second determination in the reality.

Here in the philosophy of nature and physical science we are confronted with two bodies of scientific knowledge which both concern mobile being. Is it possible to distinguish completely these two knowledges as two autonomous sciences with diverse formal objects, and to discover the ground for such a distinction in the nature of things ?

B. THE DIFFERENTIATION OF FORMAL OBJECTS

In the intellect

On the basis of what we have learned in the preceding chapter, it is possible for us immediately to determine how the formal objects of the philosophy of nature and physical science differ in the intellect. This will enable us later to determine the foundation in the thing for this distinction. For the object in the intellect is in intrinsic dependence on the object in the thing ; the intellect does not make its objects as immanent terms of its knowledge but rather sees through them the "objected" reality. If this were not so, then the objectivity of science as an account of the *real* would perish. If, therefore, we can ascertain a clear distinction between the two formal objects in the intellect, we shall be led to affirm a corresponding ground for this distinction in the thing.

As was said in the preceding chapter, the philosophy of nature visualizes mobile being in its transphenomenal nature. Its first and primary insight is into transphenomenal being

becoming, in which it discerns the transphenomenal principles
of matter and form. Moreover, all subsequent investigation
in the philosophy of nature is directed toward knowing more
clearly the transphenomenal principles of motion and of
mobile being. We have said the same thing earlier in pointing
out that where the philosophy of nature is not dianoetic in
termination, it is at least dianoetic in tendency. The phenomena or manifestations of mobile being are mere means here,
through which we come to know the nature. The formal
object in this body of knowledge may be accurately expressed
in the formula "mobile being as *mobile being*". It is not
merely the mobility of mobile being which interests us ; we
seek to understand its transphenomenal *being* as the principle
of its mobility.

But we must point out that, although they are here only
means for knowing the nature, the phenomena necessarily
fall in an implicit way into the formal object of the philosophy
of nature. No nature can be visualized except in and through
a "context" of phenomenal manifestations. Not even the most
general principles of nature can be visualized in themselves
without reference to *some* phenomena.

On the other hand, in physical science, the phenomena of
mobile being are the central concern. All of the constructions
of physical science have reference immediately or mediately
to these observable phenomena. In these phenomena what
is of primary interest to physical science is measurable quantity ; we observe in order to measure here. Thus the formal
object of physical science can be considered from two points
of view. In the first place, mobile being is here viewed under
the aspect of its phenomenality ; physical science is perinoetic
knowledge. But secondly, and more formally, this phenomenality of mobile being is viewed precisely in so far as it is
measurable ; physical science is *empiriometric* (to use Maritain's
term) knowledge. The formal object in this body of knowledge,
therefore, is expressed in the formula "mobile being as manifesting itself through measurable phenomena". We are no
longer concerned with *being*, except obliquely ; it is the sphere

of phenomena which we study, with the purpose of learning its quantitative determinations.

And yet, as we have indicated above, the being of mobile being is not altogether missed even here. It is impossible to conceive phenomena without reference to the substantial existent of which they are the phenomena. Substance remains obscurely even in the perinoetic conceptions of physics, by right on the levels of concept and law, through a methodological fiction on the level of theory. We may say that it is explicitly present with respect to its character as a substantial *extended continuum*, and implicitly present with respect to its *nature*, in the explicit conceptions of phenomena. Thus the formal object of physical science contains the transphenomenal nature of mobile being only implicitly and the phenomenal manifestations of mobile being explicitly.

How then are the formal objects *in the intellect* of the philosophy of nature and of physical science to be distinguished ? In so far as the explicit content of the abstractive visualizations of the philosophy of nature refers to the transphenomenal nature of mobile being, while that of physical science refers to the sensible manifestations of transphenomenal nature, we may discern a clear distinction between the two objects. But this cannot be said to be a *complete* distinction. For there is an overlapping of these objects at least with respect to what is implicitly contained in them.

Yet we have shown a difference in the explicit content of the two objects. Moreover, since the implicit content is in a way only *potential* with respect to visualization and since visualization and science are primarily of explicit *actuality*, it is clear that we have here two distinct bodies of scientific knowledge.

Yet even now we have not adequately distinguished the philosophy of nature from physical science. To say that these are two distinct bodies of scientific knowledge is not yet to say that they are two distinct sciences. For if the immateriality of the object of abstractive visualization is the same in each body of knowledge, then they will reduce, in the last analysis, to one and the same science of mobile being.

However, that such is not the case may be seen by looking once more at the content of these objects. It is at once apparent that the object of the philosophy of nature is more immaterial than that of physical science. In the philosophy of nature there is only indirect attention to the sphere of operation ; our explicit concern is with the immobile principles of mobile being. On the other hand, in physical science we are no longer explicitly concerned with the nature of these immobile principles of mobile being but with its manifestation through motion itself. Since matter is the ultimate root of mobility, the object of the philosophy of nature is therefore more immaterial than the object of physical science. [1]

This lesser immateriality of the object of physical science would render science here much less unified, were it not for the employment of mathematical or logical structures as unifying principles. But since these structures are employed, the unity of physical science is even more apparent than that of the philosophy of nature ; for we can attain the perfection of scientific knowledge better in the domains of mathematics and logic than in any other.

C. THE DIFFERENTIATION OF FORMAL OBJECTS

In the thing

We have seen a differentiation of formal object *in the intellect* specifying two distinct sciences of the physical world, one philosophical and the other "physical", in the modern sense of the term. As we said earlier, corresponding to such diverse formal objects in the mind, there must always appear some diversity in the intelligibility of the thing, diverse intelligibility-appeals of second determination. [2] This is necessary since the object in the intellect intrinsically depends on and receives its determinate character as object from reality.

1. MARITAIN, *Les Degrés du Savoir*, p. 68.
2. MARITAIN, *La Philosophie de la Nature*, p. 127.

How are we to discover these roots on the side of reality, from which these diverse sciences of the physical world can come ? We may begin by returning to some considerations suggested earlier. Mobile being first of all is known to us in two ways. We have knowledge of it in its sensible manifestations and intellectual knowledge of its transphenomenal intelligible principles. This intellectual grasp of the nature is attained only through the sensible manifestations ; nevertheless we do see not merely a surface flux but the ontological depth as well.

But what is more, the intellect itself can know these very sensible manifestations in themselves—not without an obscure, mainly implicit, reference to the substantial existents which produce them but without any explicit conception of the nature of these existents. The intellect, following its natural bent, may seek to know the transphenomenal natures, using the phenomena as mere *means;* or it may resist this natural bent and focus its attention on the manifestations themselves.

Now, the transphenomenal natures are in fact really distinct from their phenomena. For the nature is as *principle* while the manifestations flow from it ; but nothing can be both principle and principiated under the same respect. This distinction of nature and manifestation is rooted in the distinction of the order of essence from the order of operation.

But this distinction is not a distinction of two *things*, or even of two *completely* distinct aspects of reality. It is only a distinction of manifestation from what is manifested. Nor must this distinction be understood in terms of Kant's "noumenon-phenomenon" dichotomy. We do not separate the phenomenon from the thing-in-itself. The intelligible nature can really be revealed, at least obscurely, through the manifestations. [1]

Thus the formal aspect of mobility is found to be radically divisible into two aspects in reality, two formal objects *in the thing*, but two which *overlap*, which flow into each other.

1. *Ibid.*, p. 129.

For the transphenomenal nature only shows itself to us through these manifestations, and these manifestations intrinsically refer to their transphenomenal principles.   This results in what we have already noted, that the *explicit* content of the concepts of the philosophy of nature is almost entirely distinct from the *explicit* content of the concepts of physical science (I say, "almost entirely," because even the concepts of phenomena include explicit awareness of a substantial extended continuum), while each of them refers *implicitly* to the explicit content of the other which it does not itself consider explicitly.

D. THE COMPLEMENTARY CHARACTER OF THE PHILOSOPHY OF
    NATURE AND PHYSICAL SCIENCE

From what we have said it follows that, despite the distinction between these sciences, they complement each other in the study of mobile being.[1]   Each attains mobile being from a different point of view.   But the two points of view must be put together to gain an integral knowledge of nature ; for each of these sciences, taken by itself, is an inadequate account of mobile being.[2]

Furthermore, we may say that each of these sciences, considered in itself, can be seen to *call for* the other.   The philosophy of nature, taken as a generic study of nature, sees its own inadequacy and tends to extend itself by more detailed and specific knowledge.   We can see this in the work of Aristotle, as we have pointed out above.   Unfortunately, Aristotle attempted to achieve this extension with the same methods as those of the general philosophy of nature, only supplemented by more detailed observation.   He continued to seek dianoetic knowledge even where it was not to be had so easily. It was necessary in fact to await the evolution of the modern sciences of phenomena, before being able properly to extend the philosophy of nature.   Even then, however, the philosophy

1. *Ibid.*, pp. 117-118.
2. *Ibid.*, p. 95.

of nature must, for the most part, content itself with constructing "philosophical myths" about the detail of nature, "myths" the construction of which may be stimulated by and proceed along lines suggested by these sciences of phenomena.

On the other hand, physical science is confronted with substantial existents the nature of which it does not know, and with a qualitative diversity which it cannot penetrate but only note and measure. Physical science is confronted with a necessity running through the contingency of the phenomena, a necessity the investigation of which lies outside its scope. Physical science calls for a philosophy of nature to treat such questions, just as the philosophy of nature calls for physical science to treat other questions.

E. THE FORMAL OBJECT AND THE METHOD OF CONCEPTUALIZATION

In our discussion, we have progressed from the method of abstractive visualization to the formal object *in the mind* to the formal object *in the thing*. This is inverse with respect to the order of being. It is the formal object *in the thing* which attracts the intellect and which ultimately specifies the science. It is in abstractively seeing the diverse formal objects *in the thing* that we obtain the formal objects *in the mind*. Once a formal object *in the thing* has presented itself through the medium of the formal object *in the mind*, it is necessary for us to devise techniques of abstractive visualization and reasoning, *methods*, with which to deepen and stabilize our attainment of this formal object. Here the mind becomes active, building logical structures and laying down rules of procedure, searching the object as deeply as it can. In the study of method, we have confined ourselves in this essay to a discussion of methods of abstractive visualization in the philosophy of nature and physical science, since this was sufficient for our purpose. *In quo sit finis et consummatio huius sermonis.*

THE DIVERSE MEANINGS OF "MATHEMATICS"

The purpose of this note is not to decide which is the most appropriate meaning at present of the term "mathematics", or what the science of mathematics ought to be or to become. Rather, it is simply to present together, in the light of Thomist thought, some widely varying meanings which have in fact been given to "mathematics" ; this will enable us to relate these meanings to each other.

Through most of the history of Western thought, the term has been used to designate the study of quantitative manifolds, a study which has traditionally been divided into arithmetic (or algebra) and geometry. But in recent times, the development of thought among mathematicians has led many of them far from the study of quantitative manifolds. In the course of this development, several diverse conceptions of mathematics have arisen. In fact, we have come to the point where it is asked whether mathematics is not really identical with logic or with grammar, or even with metaphysics.

Before actually considering these diverse meanings, it is well to review briefly the Thomist teaching on the division of speculative knowledge ; this will enable us later to understand better the exact place of each of the studies which receives the name of mathematics.

The basic division of speculative knowledge, for the Thomist, is according to the three degrees of abstraction, or separation, from matter and motion. At the first level, the object is mobile being as mobile—we have been considering principally this level in the course of the preceding essay. We have seen that there is a fundamental division at this level between the philosophy of nature and the sciences of observable phenomena.

At the third level, the object is being as being—we considered this in chapter I. Here we may add that being may be considered either as *being in reality* or as *being in the intellect;* this diversity gives rise to the distinction between metaphysics and logic.

At the second level, Thomists have traditionally recognized one generic science of quantity (considered apart from the conditions of real existence)—mathematics—which immediately subdivides into the science of discrete quantity (arithmetic) and the science of continuous quantity (geometry). But in the light of the discussions of the preceding essay, it seems necessary to distinguish quantity as an ontological mode of being and quantity as manifested in the observable or imaginable ; let us call these respectively trans-phenomenal and phenomenal quantity. This distinction gives rise to a distinction between the philosophy of quantified being and the sciences of mathematics (as the study of imaginable quantitative manifolds). The philosophy of quantified being is of greatest relevance to the philosophy of nature ; and it plays a role in relation to mathematical knowledge of phenomenal quantity somewhat analogous to that which the philosophy of nature plays in relation to the natural sciences of phenomena. But just as are the sciences of phenomena, so also the science of phenomenal quantity is autonomous with respect to its philosophical counterpart. What we have done is to extend the distinction between perinoetic and dianoetic knowledge to the second level of abstractive visualization as well as the first. This does not seem to have been done even by Maritain. Yet it is a necessary step if we are to avoid the paradox of using a science of quantity as a mode of transphenomenal being (traditional Thomist mathematics) as a necessary aid in our theoretical unification of the data given in the perinoetic knowledge of physical nature. The quantity considered in physical science is phenomenal, not transphenomenal, quantity ; accordingly the quantity of the mathematical superstructure (if this superstructure is interpreted as being itself mathematical rather than logical, and mathematical in a quantitative sense) ought itself to be phenomenal quantity rather than transphenomenal quantity.

The now refined Thomist conception of mathematics then yields at least two possible meanings for the term "mathematics". It may designate the study of transphenomenal quantitative manifolds or the study of phenomenal quantitative manifolds. But this is not all. In ancient and medieval thought, the quantitative manifolds studied were restricted quantitative manifolds : the concept of number had not been evolved so as to include such things as imaginary and transfinite numbers, and continuous quantity was not seen as able to be anything other than Euclidean.

The development of modern thought, however, has done away with this situation ; it is now necessary to distinguish between restricted quantitative manifolds (which manifest themselves directly in the imagination) and generalized quantitative manifolds (which do not so manifest themselves, but which nevertheless are still thinkable by analogy with the directly imaginable). The Thomist conception of mathematics as the study of quantitative manifolds thus now resolves into four subconcepts of mathematics. Mathematics may study either transphenomenal or phenomenal quantitative manifolds ; in either case it may study either restricted or generalized quantitative manifolds.

Some of mathematics, however, such as set theory, seems to have progressed beyond the study of quantitative manifolds to a consideration even of non-quantitative manifolds, therefore to a consideration of transcendental unity and multiplicity. Such an investigation, on Thomist principles, must be located in the domain proper to metaphysics—though of course there is nothing wrong with a mathematician becoming interested in metaphysical problems !

All of the above conceptions of mathematics have in common the fact that they present mathematics as having some determinate content. All of these conceptions can be described as "intuitionist" in a broad sense of this term. But in recent years there has been a steady trend of "mathematicians" away from the study of determinate quantitative content to the study of relations between indeterminate contents—this is the "formalist" conception of mathematics. Always mathematics has considered relations, but now the relations have become divorced from the relata ; or we may say that mathematicians have turned from the relations of content to consider only the relations of logical or grammatical formal structure. The formalist mathematician studies either relations between entirely indeterminate relata (this is really the concern of formal logic) or relations between material symbols (this is really the concern of speculative grammar). It is formalist mathematics which comes to be identified with either formal logic or grammar. And when logic and grammar themselves are identified, as in positivistic philosophy, then all three subjects are considered to be basically one, or at best diverse parts of the same one science. Mathematics may here be regarded as a part of logic, or logic as a part of mathematics.

Finally, some have entertained a "physicalist" conception of mathematics. Here mathematics is considered to be a science of the physical world. It studies quantitative manifolds as they exist in physical reality. If the concern is with real transphenomenal quantitative manifolds, then this mathematics is a part of the philosophy of nature. If, on the other hand, the concern is with real phenomenal quantitative manifolds, then this mathematics is really empiriometric science of natural phenomena, of which physical science is the preeminent part.

An analogous physicalism can be conceived even as regards mathematics in the formalist sense. If only those formal structures are regarded as truly mathematical which have some applicability in knowledge of the physical world, then we have such a physicalist formalism.

Before ending, I wish to insist once again that I am not attempting to settle the question of what *ought* to be called mathematics by all at the present time. I have myself said that certain things called mathematics are *really* something else, like logic, grammar, or metaphysics ; but this has been said in the light of the Thomist philosophical tradition, in which the term "mathematics" has a very precise significance. Those who are not Thomists (and a great portion of the modern intellectual world is not) can hardly be expected to observe the niceties of Thomist technical terminology. Nevertheless, a great deal of confusion can be removed if we do look at the matter in the light of Thomist principles. And we Thomists can in fact much more readily understand discussions which go on outside our tradition about the nature of mathematics if we habitually view the whole area in such a light. Even the little consideration we have made shows us that some modern discussions concerning the possible identification of logic and mathematics, or concerning the question of whether mathematics deals with quantitative manifolds or something else, are not the enormities they may seem to some uninformed Thomists.

THE INTERACTION OF THE PHILOSOPHY OF NATURE AND PHYSICAL SCIENCE

A. THE DEPENDENCE OF THE PHILOSOPHY OF NATURE ON PHYSICAL SCIENCE

I have already considered elsewhere [1] some ways in which the philosophy of nature can depend upon physical science. Briefly, once the philosophy of nature has been constituted in an essential core of certain knowledge about the general transphenomenal principles of motion, it is possible for this philosophy of nature to use the contents of physical science to deepen and prolong its own philosophical understanding of the principles of motion. This deepening and prolongation takes place in two ways.

If we consider the levels of concept and law in physical science, where there is immediate knowledge of the observable real, we must admit the possibility of a deepening of philosophical insight into transphenomenal nature through reflection on this content of physical science ; for nature manifests itself to us through the phenomena. On the other hand, no such deepening of insight is possible merely on the basis of the theoretical level of physical science ; for this theoretical level does not itself represent anything real but only a construction of the intellect and imagination.

Theoretical constructions of physical science can, however, suggest philosophical constructions, hypothetical natures, expressing what the transphenomenal nature of things might be like. But the physical theory cannot even do this if it is considered only as a mathematical or logical structure ; it is necessary that such a structure be embodied in a physical model before it can become a basis for philosophical hypothesis. When the theoretical structure is thus embodied, we have in effect an imaginable universe created as an "explanation" for the observable universe. Just as the observable universe is the foundation for an intellectual under-standing of the real transphenomenal natures (whether certain

1. "'Integrated' Knowledge of Nature," *The Thomist*, XXI, 2 (April, 1958), pp. 171-183.

or hypothetical), so this imaginable universe is the foundation for a hypothetical understanding of transphenomenal natures—just as the sense-data are the means for an abstractive (or else abstractive, constructive, and hypothetical) understanding of real natures, so the data of the imagination are the means for an abstractive (and at the same time constructive) understanding of hypothetical natures which are conceived as the trans-imaginable intelligible principles of these imagined data and their constructed patterns. Of course, if any such imagined data and patterns are later found to correspond to the actually observable data and patterns, the corresponding hypothetical natures acquire a much more immediate reference (though still mainly hypothetical) to the real nature of things.

In all this it must be noted that such new understanding of the actual or hypothetical natures of things may itself continue to have a certain generality or obscurity, but even so it is better than nothing at all. For examples of such use of physical science by the philosophy of nature in order to achieve a greater understanding of transphenomenal nature, I quote a few paragraphs from the above mentioned article.

"First, we may point out some permanent acquisitions, some additions which transcend the level of myth. We have become aware, through the work of science, of an exceedingly fine micro-structure in the physical universe. The facts accounted for by the modern atomic theories and by modern quantum theory also, when viewed philosophically, point out that things in the universe do not at all have the crude continuity ascribed to them in the earlier period of the philosophy of nature.

"Similarly, we have become aware of the presence of life on a much smaller and varied scale than the ancients had dreamed of.

"Then too, the telescope has revealed to us the fine structure of the heavens. No more do we think in terms of some seventy or so crystalline spheres. Now we see a diversity of galactic and extra-galactic nebulae, of galactic and globular clusters, of multiple stars, such as would astound our ancestors. Not that we are at all certain as to *what* this diversity really is (we often attribute far more certitude to astronomy than it really possesses) ; but at least we know that it is there.

"We have also come to see the dominant character of the *relative* in the physical universe, the difficulty, if not the impossibility, of finding absolute standards with which to quantitatively measure physical reality.

"Philosophical myths about the physical universe are becoming more and more difficult to construct, with the evolution of more and more complex scientific theories. Where, not too long ago, it was not too difficult to construct such myths on the basis of mechanistic philosophy, it is extremely difficult to do so now. On the other hand, Whitehead's suggestion that now we need an interpretation of science in terms of a "philosophy of organism" is full of meaning for Thomism. For Thomism is a philosophy which recognizes the organicity of matter on the level of living things as coming from a unitary form from which will flow many activities. It is equally able to account for an organicity on the level of non-living things if we ascertain the presence of such organicity.

"The modern physical models of the atom readily suggest an application of the concept of organism. It is possible for the Thomist to construct an ideal essence from which would flow just such an organic structure. This ideal essence would itself, of course, be only mythical.

"The diversity of parts of an organism is due to the naturally diverse accidental dispositions of matter in the diverse parts of the extended being. We may, perhaps, apply this notion of organism even to the entire space-time continuum as visualized in Einsteinian general relativity, a continuum which is constantly changing in the states of its diverse parts in space and time. Indeed, matter itself might even be metaphysically assimilated to this philosophically interpreted space-time continuum, in a way not yet explained, on the lower levels of material existence. Once again, we are speaking of a mythical essence." [1]

B. THE DEPENDENCE OF PHYSICAL SCIENCE ON THE PHILOSOPHY OF NATURE

The phenomenal flux and the underlying "substantial extension" necessarily revealed through this phenomenal flux constitute the given for the physical scientist as such. But if this were all that

1. *Ibid.*, pp. 180-181.

he could see, the chaos of the phenomena and the lack of inner differentiation in the "substantial extension" could only discourage any attempt at scientific knowledge of this domain of being. The hope for scientific knowledge of this phenomenal world, for the eventual understanding of an order in the phenomena, can be aroused only if some other source of knowledge about the physical real can be found. It is not sufficient to appeal to a purely subjective conviction, to a purely a priori attitude ; for our actual hope of finding such order in the phenomenal world is not merely subjective. It is forced upon us willy-nilly by the world itself.

Hume rightly points out that no objective ground exists for it in the phenomena themselves. Nevertheless, his belief that it is purely subjective does not deter him from acting as all men who wish to stay alive act—namely, on the supposition that such a determinate order of things does in fact exist independently of us. Nor is this supposition irrational ; no one except the insane believes that it would be rational to act in any other manner. And it is only the philosopher in the quiet of his study, or in academic discussion, who can raise the theoretical difficulties of Hume, as he himself admits. When we come back to the business of living, all such difficulties disappear and we spontaneously accept the existence of the determinate order of things.

Kant's appeal to a pure a priori to account for this spontaneous acceptance of the fact of a determinate order in the phenomena is likewise inadequate to account for what we know. We can distinguish between ourselves and the rest of the universe, between our knowledge and the reality of things ; and we find an order to exist in the things themselves. Our primary immediate consciousness is not of our imposing an order on the things but of the things manifesting their own intrinsic order to us. Later, in the sciences of phenomena, we also impose an order on things ; but this is not the primary given. We impose this secondary order because of our prior conviction, forced upon us by reality itself, that things themselves do have a determinate order.

But whence can this awareness of order intrinsic to the things themselves come, since Hume has rightly pointed out that it cannot be derived from the knowledge of phenomena themselves ? In the preceding essay we have pointed out the existence of knowledge of the transphenomenal nature of things. It is in this transphenomenal domain that the roots of phenomenal order are to be found.   In the transphenomenal domain we discover a determinate order of substantial existents intrinsically differentiated and interacting as agents for determinate ends.   The obscure awareness of this transphenomenal reality is, of course, common to all men ; it is the purpose of the philosophy of nature to clarify, deepen, and expand this knowledge, so far as this is possible.

We have here the primary dependence of physical science upon the philosophy of nature.   The hope of discovering order in the phenomena, a hope without which the dynamic movement of physical science would never even begin, is aroused through the at least obscure awareness of the transphenomenal order of substantial natures, agents, and ends, through knowledge which belongs to the proper domain of the philosophy of nature.

But even beyond arousing the hope of discovering order in the phenomena, this transphenomenal knowledge provides us with transphenomenal nuclei around which to group the phenomena we investigate.   The first ordering of even the phenomena themselves, an ordering which is presupposed for the eventual development of physical concepts and laws, is the immediate reflection in the phenomenal order of the transphenomenal order of natures. I consider this set of phenomena as distinguished from that set of phenomena because here I have one substance (e. g. this man) and there I have another substance (e. g. that dog).   I make a first (somewhat vague) correlation of phenomena in two distinct things because I am aware of a transphenomenal causal influence of one on the other, or of each upon the other.   Of course, it is true that I must first know the general correlation of phenomena in order to come to know the causal dependence ; but this first knowledge of correlation is merely factual and instrumental to the transphenomenal knowledge.   Only in the light of such achieved transphenomenal knowledge does this (itself still vague) correlation of phenomena themselves acquire a certain (extrinsic) necessity.

At this point it is appropriate to say a few words concerning the genesis of physical concepts under the influence of transphenomenal knowledge.   I do not have in mind, however, those physical concepts which are developed once a theoretical structure is already in existence, but rather such physical concepts as must be evolved before the theoretical structure can come into being.   Of course, there is always a mutual influence between concept and theory, with the concepts themselves being modified in order to achieve a still simpler theory. But I wish, as far as possible, to consider the genesis of a concept in independence of such theoretical influence ; this will enable us better to see the proper influence of trans-phenomenal knowledge in the genesis of the physical concept.

Six steps may be distinguished : (1) Some at least obscure trans-phenomenal knowledge of some aspect of physical reality is given ; (2) This transphenomenal element is taken as a nucleus around which are grouped the associated phenomena ; (3) A complex concept is formed, consisting of the transphenomenal element and a perinoetic concept of the associated phenomena ; (4) Ways of measuring the central phenomenon of the phenomenal complex are determined ; (5) Other such intermediate complex concepts may also be formed, of other phenomenal groupings around the same transphenomenal nucleus, and corresponding modes of measurement developed ; (6) The transphenomenal nucleus drops out of the picture entirely—at this point it is necessary that the diverse perinoetic concepts corresponding to a given nucleus be linked to each other through the theoretical structure of physical science itself, since the transphenomenal principle of integration has now been dropped in order to achieve a completely perinoetic knowledge.

I present these six steps only as a *possible* explanation of the process. They may be exemplified in the following consideration of a possible development of the concept of mass.

(1) We become aware that bodies resist what tends to change their state of local motion. We consider such resistance to be a property arising from the very nature of material being.

(2) We relate this property to the phenomenal manifestation of resistance to pushes and pulls, perhaps in particular to some ob-servable manner of weighing a body, e. g. the use of a spring scale.

(3) The whole phenomenal complex arising from the use of a spring scale is now conceptualized perinoetically, and this concept is correlated with the concept of the above-mentioned ontological property of resistance.

(4) A technique of determinate measurement is developed through the calibration of the spring scale.

(5) A similar procedure may take place in developing parallel perinoetic concepts corresponding to the same ontological property of resistance, e. g. the concept of the use of a mass-spectrograph, the concept of the use of a chemical balance, etc. All of these are

here linked to the concept of the ontological property of resistance.

(6) Gradually, the ontological property of resistance is disregarded ; and the diverse perinoetic concepts of mass become linked to each other in the framework of the physical theory and laws.

So much for the genesis of physical concepts under the influence of transphenomenal knowledge. We may now say a few words concerning the influence of such transphenomenal knowledge on the development of theoretical structures and models in physical science.

In the previous section of this Appendix, we saw that a movement was possible from theoretical structure to embodying image to at least hypothetical understanding of the nature of things. The reverse movement also seems possible and indeed a fact in physical science. A philosophical view of the nature of things gives rise to an "image" of the world ; and this image suggests the kind of theoretical structure which the physical scientist attempts to create.

In fact, these two movements, from philosophy to theoretical physical science and from theoretical physical science to philosophy, are ordinarily very much entangled with each other. But just as we ignored one side in the previous section, so here we can ignore the other in giving some general examples of the influence of philosophy upon the theoretical development of physical science.

Philosophical mechanism suggests the use of mechanical models and a "particle physics". When philosophical determinism is accepted, the fundamental "laws" of physics (at the theoretical level) must be classical rather than statistical. Statistical laws are invoked only where the application of classical laws becomes impracticable because of the large numbers of entities involved, or some similar reason. If reality is ultimately regarded as a continuum rather than as a set of discrete entities, field-physics will be preferred to particle-physics, neo-classical Einsteinian physics to quantum physics. (Of course, the truth is that these diverse physics are each successful in its own way—an indication that the philosophy underlying each is not a complete philosophy.) One wonders where a generally accepted philosophical view of organic and hylomorphic structure in the universe would lead the development of physical theory. Such a view has certainly been suggested by the developments of physical science—Einstein's tendency to regard the universe as fundamentally continuous, the loss of the complete distinction between wave and particle in quantum physics, along with the necessity of preserving this distinction in some form, resulting in the enunciation of the "complementarity principle" for the description of the physical universe ; and the general acceptance of the concept of organic evolution in the biological sciences itself reflects backward into the physical sciences, for there is some continuity between the living and the non-living in the universe.

If indeed the nature of the physical universe is in fact at bottom both organic and hylomorphic, as Thomists generally maintain, then the Thomist philosophy of nature—deepened and broadened— should provide a new stimulus for the development and integration of physical theory. But, of course, philosophers of nature do not usually cultivate physical science and physical scientists are usually content with the obscure beginnings of a philosophy of nature. For the present, the experiment remains untried.

So much for the genesis of physical concept and theory under the influence of transphenomenal knowledge. One final dependence of physical science upon such transphenomenal knowledge remains to be noted. Even supposing that physical concepts and theories have been evolved, there still remains the problem of deciding which of these concepts and theories are applicable to that segment of the phenomenal flux which here and now falls under considera-tion, and how the application is to be made. We have already admitted that the phenomena do not exhibit an intrinsic order. But if this is so, then the phenomenal data will not tell us how to apply our conceptual apparatus. Yet this application, for a physical scientist, is not mere guesswork. He knows when his electro-magnetic theory and concepts become relevant, and he knows when mechanics is sufficient to understand a phenomenon—or at least he feels fairly certain about it.

It seems necessary that knowledge of the transphenomenal nuclei referred to above exercises here a certain normative influence from outside physical science itself. The procedure is somewhat analogous to that in the first formation of the notions of physical science. But now it is easier and more rapid - at the beginning it was necessary to evolve step by step the conceptual apparatus ; but now this conceptual apparatus is already at hand waiting to be applied to the understanding of the phenomena under this guidance from transphenomenal insight, however obscure this transphenomenal insight may be.

It seems appropriate at this moment to insert a parenthetical note concerning the obscurity of most of this transphenomenal knowledge. It is necessary to see that, in view of the characteristic weakness of the human intellect, the obscurity of a knowledge does not necessarily diminish its importance. Physical science can achieve much greater clarity over much wider areas than can the philosophy of nature. But this is in great part due to the fact that it does not penetrate the being of the physical universe in as profound a manner as does the philosophy of nature - the price of profound penetration is most often a degree of obscurity in knowledge. Nevertheless, this obscure transphenomenal knowledge has the greatest importance for physical science, as we have seen above.

Finally, the impossibility of pure empiricism in physical science, together with an inability or refusal to recognize the value of such transphenomenal insight as we have, have led many—especially Kant, and Eddington in his footsteps—to postulate a completely a priori knowledge in the human mind. I believe that they are correct in their fundamental intuition that there must be some knowledge a priori with respect to the phenomena as such if a physical science of observable phenomena is to come into being at all. But they are mistaken in conceiving it as an absolute a priori; it arises in virtue of the transphenomenal insight, frequently quite obscure, which belongs to the domain of the philosophy of nature and metaphysics, even if this insight has not been sufficiently clarified to constitute a scientific knowledge in either of these domains.

SUMMARY BIBLIOGRAPHY

ARISTOTLE. *Aristotelis De Caelo et De Generatione et Corruptione.* Recensuit Carolus Prantl. Lipsiae : in aedibus B. G. Teubneri, 1881.
— *Aristotle's Physics.* Edited by W. D. Ross. London : Oxford University Press, 1936.
— *Prior and Posterior Analytics.* Edited by W. D. Ross. Oxford : Clarendon Press, 1949.

BORN, Max. *Experiment and Theory in Physics.* New York : Dover Publications, 1956.

BRIDGMAN, P. W. *The Logic of Modern Physics.* New York : The Macmillan Company, 1927.

CAJETAN, Thomas de Vio. *In De Ente et Essentia D. Thomae Aquinatis Commentaria.* P. M.-H. Laurent, editor. Taurini : Marietti, 1934.
— *Tractatus De Subjecto Naturalis Philosophiae.* Edited by C. De Koninck and R. P. E. Gaudron, O. F. M. Quebec : Editions Laval, 1939.
— *Commentaria in Summam Theologicam S. Thomae Aquinatis.* In editioni Leonina. Romae : 1888-1906. Vol. IV.

CARNAP, R. "Testability and Meaning," *Philosophy of Science,* 3 (1936) and 4 (1937).

DUHEM, Pierre. *The Aim and Structure of Physical Theory.* Translated by Philip P. Wiener. Princeton : Princeton University Press, 1954.

EDDINGTON, Sir Arthur. *The Nature of the Physical World.* New York : The Macmillan Company, 1929.
— *The Philosophy of Physical Science.* Cambridge : Cambridge University Press, 1949.

EINSTEIN, Albert. *The Meaning of Relativity.* 5th edition. Princeton : Princeton University Press, 1955.

— *Relativity*. Translated by R. W. Lawson. 15th edition. London : Methuen, 1955.

— "The Fundaments of Theoretical Physics," *Science*, 91 (1940).

EINSTEIN, A. and INFELD, L. *The Evolution of Physics*. New York : Simon and Schuster, 1938.

FRANK, Philipp. *Philosophy of Science*. Englewood Cliffs, New Jersey : Prentice-Hall, 1957.

HUME, David. *An Inquiry Concerning Human Understanding*. New York : The Liberal Arts Press, 1955.

JOHN OF ST. THOMAS. *Ars Logica. Cursus Philosophicus Thomisticus*. Vol. I. Ed. Reiser. Taurini : Marietti, 1930.

— *Philosophia Naturalis. Cursus Philosophicus Thomisticus*. Vol. II. Ed. Reiser. Taurini : Marietti, 1933.

KANT, Immanuel. *Critique of Pure Reason*. Translated by N. K. Smith. New York : Humanities Press, 1950.

MARGENAU, H. *The Nature of Physical Reality*. New York : McGraw-Hill, 1950.

MARITAIN, Jacques. *Les Degrés du Savoir*. Paris : Desclée De Brouwer, 1932.

— *La Philosophie de la Nature*. Paris : Tequi, 1935.

— *Quatre Essais sur l'Esprit dans sa condition charnelle*. Nouvelle éd. rev. et aug. Paris : Alsatia, 1956.

— *Réflexions sur l'Intelligence et sur sa vie propre*. 4th ed. Paris : Desclée De Brouwer, 1938.

MARTIN, Oliver. *The Order and Integration of Knowledge*. Ann Arbor : The University of Michigan Press, 1957.

NEWTON, Isaac. *Mathematical Principles*. Revised translation by F. Cajori. Berkeley : University of California Press, 1947.

POINCARÉ, H. *Science and Hypothesis*. New York : Dover Publications, 1952.

SMITH, Vincent. *Philosophical Physics*. New York : Harper and Bros., 1950.

ST. THOMAS AQUINAS. *Opera omnia*.

WHITEHEAD, A. N. *Science and the Modern World*. New York : Mentor Books, 1956.

INDEX OF NAMES

ANALYTIC INDEX

Imprimé en Belgique

ACHEVÉ D'IMPRIMER SUR LES PRESSES
DE L'IMPRIMERIE SAINT-AUGUSTIN
À BRUGES, LE 14 JANVIER 1966
POUR LES ÉDITIONS
DESCLÉE DE BROUWER

101.11.02